Wakefield

PLANTS IN HIS PACK

Plants in His Pack is the story of Edward Palmer, a long-forgotten scientific collector who devoted his entire life to gathering the wondrous plants, animals, birds, and Indian artifacts from the wild frontiers of the American West and Mexico. By canal boat, stagecoach, muleback, and finally railroad, he traveled on his endless quest for new and different plants. Neither hostile Indians nor the hardships of the open trail deterred this lone explorer during his sixty long years of field work in some of the wildest spots on this continent. He spent the Civil War years as an army doctor in the West, combating arrow wounds and malaria, but gathering plants whenever his ambulance wagon chanced to stop. Later he worked among the Kiowas, Comanches, Wichitas, and Apaches, bringing back sheaves of information about their strange customs. He was the first scientist to explore remote Guadalupe Island off Lower California and to dig into the ancient Indian ruins of Utah and Arizona. He alone collected more than 100,000 different plants for museums and universities in America and Europe. Yet after his death in 1911 he was all but forgotten, and only a quirk of fate finally brought his remarkable career to light.

Plants in His Pack is the compelling biography of a remarkable man who in the pursuit of scientific knowledge lived the adventurous life of the American pioneer.

Plants in His

A Life of Edward Palmer,

Pack

Adventurous Botanist and Collector

by JANICE J. BEATY

Illustrations by JOAN BERG

Pantheon Books

TO JIM

ACKNOWLEDGMENTS

My deep appreciation and grateful thanks go to Mary
Drinker Elek, editor of *Frontiers* (Academy of Natural
Sciences of Philadelphia) for having published my first
Edward Palmer article; to Rogers McVaugh for his
comprehensive Palmer bibliography; to the Special
Collections, the Science Library, and the Herbarium at the
University of Arizona, Tucson; to the staffs of the Phoenix
Public Library and the Arizona State Library, Phoenix;
to Dessie Miller of the Buckeye Library; and to my husband
for his endless patience and helpful criticism.

Contents

E D W A R D   P A L M E R

1831-1911

The Fens

1

The Fens

Edward Palmer straddled the rail of the heavy sailing barge and stared down at his reflection in the narrow drainage canal. He was thin, always too thin to be really healthy. He was dark — his mother's black eyes and hair, people said. And he was handsome; he scowled at the face that attracted so much attention from the fair sex. Edward Palmer, aged eighteen, was the shyest young man in Wilton village, Norfolk county, England.

Suddenly the image blurred as the barge shuddered to life. Her sails filled and they were off, hauling the first of the summer's farm produce to the market at Brandon town.

Palmer kept to himself, as was his usual habit. The crude jokes and constant teasing of the boatmen had once annoyed him, but not any more. He was used to such talk by now and simply ignored it. Long ago he had learned that few people shared his burning interests. The less he said to other folks, the better off he always seemed to be.

He remembered the first time he had come aboard with his produce. Not a bulging sack of potatoes, nor a brace of wild ducks, nor even a hamper of marsh eels, but flowers: neat bundles of marigolds, daffodils, and calendulas, every one of them grown by his hand in his own garden.

Flowers had always been a part of his life. As far back as Edward Palmer could remember, he had been drawn to the wild flowers in the few remaining marshes near the village. He had gathered their blooms, much to the amusement of his older brother, William. He had experimented with wild seeds and bulbs and cuttings. "Weeds," his mother had scoffed. But his father — God rest his soul — his father had nodded wisely and begun instructing him in the art of growing real flowers, just as the old man himself had done in his younger days before the rheumatism had crippled him so.

And in spite of the boatmen and all their remarks, he had sold his flowers to the vendors in Brandon — every one of them, just as he would do again this season. He was a successful flower grower like his father before him. You had to have a special touch to grow flowers, his father always said, and he, Edward, had it. A success at eighteen. Not many young Wilton men could make that boast. And yet . . . Palmer shifted restlessly.

What was it that always made him feel somehow dissatisfied? The memory of the long-lost wild flowers he had put aside to grow commercial blooms? How could that be? Wild or not, flowers were flowers, weren't they?

He looked out over the passing country and sighed. His homeland — the flat, flat Fens. The Fens looked like Holland, people said. They were rich marshlands reclaimed from the sea, drained by ditches, bounded by dikes, and pumped dry by creaking windmills at every crossover. Then, cleared and plowed and planted. Wonderful farmlands. The best in England. And yet . . .

Gone were the wild acres of marsh grass glistening in the sun. Gone were the herons and tiger swallowtails and water snakes that had made his early years so exciting, his years of hiking and tramping and exploring the marshes, alone but never lonely in the world of wild things around him. Now not a single marsh hawk skimmed low over cultivated gardens, and the churring call of the sedge warbler was noticeably missing. As Palmer scanned the rich farmlands from the slowly moving barge, he saw not one wild marsh, not one thicket of reeds nor patch of pond lilies.

The broad hand of a boatman clapped him across the shoulders as the man went into gales of laughter over some joke Palmer had only half heard. He edged away in embarrassment. These people around him . . . they meant well. They were honest and cheerful and hard-working. But he felt so uncomfortable in their midst, even among his own family, especially now that his father was dead.

Why should a grown man continue to collect butterflies, his mother wanted to know. And when you went fishing, you were supposed to bring home fish to eat, his brother chided, not minnows to keep in a pot of water to look at. Their only concern with wild things was that of practical folks: Was it good to eat? or, How much could you sell it for? Palmer shook his head. Some days he almost felt like staying aboard the barge at Brandon and continuing on and on. Where? To the Broads, the shallow lakes of northeast Norfolk? To the sea? Beyond?

Only his flowers gave Edward Palmer a measure of contentment. As long as he could grow them in peace, he would not complain. With plants of any kind he felt at ease. But with flowers he could lose himself completely, never failing to marvel at their myriad colors, their infinite variety of shapes and forms.

The barge thumped to a halt against the bank at Brandon town. Farmers began unloading their wares. Palmer set about searching for the flower vendors. Townsfolk he approached shook their heads in wonder. Flower vendors? Where had he been all spring? No one was buying flowers this season. What with times so bad and money so scarce, it was all a man could do to keep his cupboard stocked. Flowers? Bah!

A stunned Edward Palmer returned home that evening only to have his despair doubled. His brother William, now head of the family, had decided that the flower beds must go. They must be dug up and planted in potatoes while there was still time to raise a cash crop. Flowers had always been impractical, added William, with a smug I-told-you-so.

With every spadeful of broken stems and roots Palmer turned under in the days that followed, a new resolution grew stronger within him. His life here was finished. He would leave it all. He would move to some new land where flowers still grew wild, to some new world . . . to *the* New World. Why not? A family of friends was bound for America the very next week. He would go along!

Thus it came about that the English Fen Country sent another of its native sons across the Atlantic to make his mark in the New World — or so we must guess. The known facts of Edward Palmer's remarkable career do not begin until he steps ashore on the docks of New York in the summer of 1849.

New York in 1850

2

New York

The Atlantic crossing, although cold and rough and stormy, had one unexpected effect on the young Palmer. It infected him with an incurable love for travel. True, he had ever been on the go, exploring the marshes, sailing the waterways, tramping the byways of England, but always within a confined space. Now those ties of homeland were broken and the world was his. Even at this early stage Palmer must have realized that this first long journey would not be his last.

What did he expect of the New World? Just that: a "new world," something fresh and different. He was Columbus . . . John Cabot . . . Henry Hudson . . . all in one, the day he stepped ashore at New York. His country boy's awe and wonder over the bustling "Empire City" he kept to himself. He took in everything around him,

9

but with his usual solemn, silent scrutiny. In spare moments he began writing down detailed descriptions of everything he saw, in letters to his mother and his brother and anyone else who he thought might be interested. His plans for the future were vague. First he had to see New York.

New York in 1849 was something to see. There was wide and wonderful Broadway a-rumble with gaily painted omnibuses. You took your life in your hands to cross its endless streams of horse-drawn traffic. Splendid brick mansions, magnificent hotels, and imposing marble stores lined the avenue. The sidewalks swarmed with Irish and Germans fresh off the boat, dapper young businessmen rushing madly everywhere, and elegant society ladies with always a smile for the good-looking but bashful young Englishman.

Palmer must have visited Barnum's great Museum, the best-known amusement attraction in the country. He certainly saw a minstrel show, then all the rage. Perhaps he even viewed New York from the cupola atop City Hall. Nor could he have missed the Astor House hotel, the "marble palace" department store, nor the dazzling new ice-cream "saloons."

If there was something worth seeing, Edward Palmer certainly saw it. He was forever attracted to and fascinated by the new and the different, whether in the wilds of a marsh or on the cobblestones of a city. And just to make sure he would always remember the event, he began saving theater playbills, ticket stubs, and newspaper clippings showing places he had visited.

He may have taken a ride over to Jersey on the new

steam ferry for half a penny. And how he must have been drawn to the East River piers where a forest of tall-masted clipper ships awaited swarms of eager gold-rushers bound around Cape Horn for California! "Oh! Susannah," they sang in rousing chorus as one by one their trim vessels slipped from narrow berths and hoisted sail. Much as he must have been tempted, Palmer was not yet ready for California. There was an entire continent before him, and he did not intend to skip any of it.

Yet boats were the only practical means of travel west in 1849. Roads were still wagon ruts between towns, with miles of impassable mountains intervening. Railroads were only beginning their westward creep. It was the great water highways that carried America west before mid-nineteenth century. And New York was situated at the head of the greatest of them: the Hudson River–Erie Canal–Great Lakes route.

The day Palmer boarded the Hudson River steamer for Albany goes unrecorded, but it must have been a gay one. The steamers were large, luxuriously outfitted vessels, always bursting with excited travelers, fresh and eager and full of high hopes for the new life awaiting them at the end of the line.

Yet the trip up the Hudson was a tame one indeed, compared to the roisterous canal jaunt from Albany to Buffalo. Americans took the serious business of moving entire families across a country in a most lighthearted manner, Palmer must have noted.

The canal packet he boarded was long and low, jammed with nearly a hundred voyagers. Its ninety-foot length was almost all cabin, one huge room for eating and sleeping — all together. Being short of stature, Palmer could stand up straight inside, but some of the lanky Americans spent most of their time ducking the low-beamed ceiling.

The Erie Canal was on a much grander scale than anything he had known in the Fens. It ran for 363 miles, with eighty-three locks lifting the boats to the higher level of Lake Erie and eighteen aqueducts lifting the canal itself over intersecting rivers. Some of the canal locks were among the man-made "wonders of America" listed in every tourist guide. At Lockport, for instance, Palmer must have gazed in awe at the immense but narrow man-made canyon where five pairs of locks climbed steplike through solid rock to the top of the Niagara plateau.

He must have observed his fellow passengers with just as much interest. Most of the ladies would spend the day on the roof of the cabin, which served as deck, lounging in low-backed "settles." It was amusing to see them duck every time the towpath driver called out, "Low bridge!" There were three hundred low bridges between Albany and Utica, a third of the way to Buffalo!

Many of the men would spend the entire day gambling in the "saloon," as the cabin was called during the day. Although Palmer disapproved, he could hardly help but watch with interest the ingenious games they invented. Races between cockroaches or grasshoppers or frogs were the most popular. They were placed on the table in the center of a huge chalk circle. The first one out of the circle won. Palmer must have been tempted to retrieve the creatures to see how they compared with those of England.

Many of the younger men were too restless to abide

the leisurely pace of the packets. They would hop onto the bank, trot along the towpath, and then drop back onto the boat from the next bridge. They were forever urging the captain to challenge passing boats to a race. Then they would seize the towline and heave with all their might, much to the relief of the hard-worked horses.

But it was the magnificent scenery that stirred Edward Palmer most of all. Here was wild America, much of it still wilderness — rolling, thickly wooded hills, glens cleft deep in fern-bedecked hillsides, swamps that stretched to the horizon. The vast Cayuga marshes at Montezuma must have gladdened the heart of an old marsh dweller like Palmer. While the others ducked below to escape the mosquito hordes, Palmer remained on deck to revel in the sight of pink swamp hibiscus the size of a dinner plate, fat beavers sunning themselves on their stick igloos, or an American bald eagle surveying its realm from the top of the tallest tree.

Palmer's interest in the passing wildlife did not go unnoticed. One passenger was particularly attracted to the alert young Englishman. At least, we suspect that is how Dr. Jared P. Kirtland first met Edward Palmer. Dr. Kirtland was returning to his home in Cleveland, Ohio. He was delighted to find a nature lover like himself aboard and willing to share some of his time during the long days ahead.

Palmer, for his part, could not have found a more perfect guide for his first tour through wild America. But the older man was much more than a nature lover. He was a professor, an author, an editor, a doctor, and a founder of the Cleveland Medical College; indeed, one of

13 | 🌳

the most prominent and respected men of the Midwest. By the time the two of them had boarded the Lake Erie steamer at Buffalo, Palmer had already accepted the doctor's invitation to stop off for a while at Cleveland.

Dr. Kirtland wanted to put him up at his own home, but it was not in Palmer's nature to be dependent on anyone. Instead, he accepted the doctor's offer to arrange for him to earn his own bed and board. Though the facts are hazy, we can well imagine that was how he came to live in the nearby home of John W. Taylor.

This second American acquaintance was just as distinguished as his first, for John W. Taylor had been a famous Speaker of the House of Representatives. He was now elderly and hopelessly crippled, and Palmer went to live with him as his personal attendant.

Things were far from dull in the Taylor household despite the Speaker's ailment. The explosive question of slavery was the main topic of the day. Taylor's violent objection to it made for lively debates among the prominent Clevelanders who would drop in of an evening. Young Palmer listened intently.

He was even more excited by their talk of international affairs. Attempts had recently been made to open Japan to the western world. Now the talk was all of Paraguay, the hermit nation of South America, and how the United States should "open" her as well. Travel to faraway places! The mere mention of it could stir him.

Strangely enough, the self-taught English country boy did not feel a bit out of place among these learned gentlemen. On the contrary, for the first time in his life Edward Palmer felt at ease among his fellow men.

His hours spent at Dr. Kirtland's proved even more fruitful. Not only was the doctor's library at his disposal, but also his wonderful collection of pressed plants and animal and bird skins. Like many a wealthy, scientifically inclined gentlemen of the day, Dr. Kirtland maintained his own private natural history collection, much in the manner of stamp or coin collectors today.

When he realized what an able and devoted pupil Palmer promised to be, he promptly began instructing him in the preparation of bird skins and the drying and pressing of plants. Somehow these tedious, rather unpleasant tasks appealed to Palmer. Perhaps he felt that through such work he was making a contribution to science. When new plants arrived, he was as enthusiastic as the doctor in trying to identify them, and just as overjoyed whenever they proved to be rare ones.

Think of it: a world of plants and living creatures still unknown, unnamed! Any man could go out and discover a new one, just for the looking. This was part of the great scientific drive of the nineteenth century. The famous Swedish naturalist, Carolus Linnaeus, had paved the way the century before with his two-word Latin naming system for every plant and animal. Now museums, universities, and private individuals were clamoring for new specimens to identify and study.

Palmer's role in this golden age of natural history was as yet unclear. But one thing he knew from the very beginning: this was his world. He could never again be happy away from it.

Then in 1852 the most incredible opportunity presented itself. The United States government actually de-

cided to send an expedition to Paraguay, just as Speaker
Taylor had been urging. What a fabulous chance for
America to collect rare and unknown specimens of plant
and animal life, Dr. Kirtland reasoned. Now, if only he
could place the industrious young Palmer aboard the expedition vessel. When the doctor learned that the cruise
would be headed by Lieutenant Thomas Jefferson Page,
an acquaintance of his, he was sure Palmer could obtain
a position.

Soon Palmer was packing for a hurried trip to Washington, armed with a letter of introduction from the doctor. He tells of his meeting with the expedition leader in
his own words:

> When I called on Lieutenant Page and explained my
> mission, he held up both hands and exclaimed: "You
> are the very man I have been looking for for the last
> six months." He told me to report to him at the Navy
> Yard the next day. I did so and was enlisted as
> hospital steward. In addition to caring for the sick
> and dispensing medicines under the direction of the
> ship's surgeon I was to collect plants and take care
> of all other collections made by officers of the
> expedition. (From Original Unpublished Manuscript
> by William E. Safford)

Edward Palmer was on his way.

3

Paraguay

Palmer had just turned twenty-two the year he boarded the *Water Witch* at her berth in the Washington naval yards. His dark eyes glistened with hard-to-conceal excitement at the very thought of the venture. Not only was he bound for an unknown land full of strange and exotic plants, but on a navy man-of-war as well. The *Water Witch* was a sleek side-wheel steamer of four hundred tons, with masts fore and aft, a tall black stack amidships, and three bronze howitzers for defense. Hers was to be a tour of good will to Paraguay, as well as a voyage of exploration along the little-known La Plata river system.

Strange, land-locked Paraguay was one of the least-known countries of South America. For years tyrannical rulers had kept her secure from the outside world by

Corumbá
Forte Coimbra
Paraguai
PARAGUAY
Paraguay
Asunción
Paraguay
Paraná
Corrientes
Tobaco Island
ARGENTINA
Paraná
La Paz
URUGUAY
Diamante
Paraná
Buenos Aires
Montevedeo
N
E

sealing off her only avenue of entry, the thousand-mile La Plata–Paraná–Paraguay river route. Forts lined its banks. Chains stretched from shore to shore at narrow passes. And then only a year ago, in 1852, her latest dictator, Carlos López, had agreed to open Paraguay rivers to the free navigation of the world.

Here was a golden opportunity for the United States. Unlimited profit lay in wait for the first nation that could sign a trade agreement with López. But what of the long river route? Could an ocean steamer ascend the thousand miles to Asunción, the Paraguay capital? What about rapids, treacherous sand bars, and sunken trees? Lieutenant Page, captain of the *Water Witch*, was assigned to take the steamer as far as possible up the three La Plata rivers leading to Paraguay. He was to chart the main channel, explore the tributaries, and report on agricultural and commercial opportunities. He was also to collect natural history specimens, and, if possible, negotiate a treaty of trade with Paraguay.

As the trim vessel began its historic voyage south, Palmer's excitement was somewhat dampened when he found himself assigned below to eat and bunk with the crew. True, he was of their age, but he was not one of them. Few if any of the fifty sailors aboard the *Water Witch* shared his scientific fervor. He had hoped to discuss natural history collecting with someone like Captain Page or the officers. But living with the crew prevented this. There was a strict line drawn between naval officers and common seamen. Civilian Palmer found himself somewhere in between.

Palmer had little time for regrets. Dr. Carter, the ship's

surgeon and his immediate superior, soon had him busy in the dispensary. Keeping it in order, preparing and dispensing medicines, and reading medical books filled his days.

From the doctor he learned that the *Water Witch* was a regular ship in the U. S. Navy's Brazilian squadron. Congress had not set aside extra money for this La Plata expedition. That meant it would have to be performed by the navy above and beyond its regular duties. Scientific equipment was at a minimum, only a few chronometers donated by the Naval Observatory, and some materials for preserving specimens contributed by the Smithsonian Institution. Trained scientists were totally lacking. Several of the officers specialized in geography and map making, and Captain Page had a keen interest in botany, but Palmer himself was the only true naturalist aboard.

He also learned that the *Water Witch* was something of an experimental vessel. Her side paddle-wheel was the latest Morgan model, with a vertical drive. This was to be the first test of its usefulness. There had been dire predictions that she would never reach Paraguay. However, she steamed along merrily, taking in stride the stormiest weather the Atlantic could hurl her way. Her supreme test came in April off the southern coast of Brazil when one of the wild *pampero* gales swept out to sea like a hurricane. Monstrous waves nearly submerged the vessel, but her Morgan wheel never faltered and soon the storm was past.

The *Water Witch* rounded the southern coast of Uruguay at night. The Rio de la Plata lay unseen before them, an immense but shallow estuary 138 miles wide. Much to Captain Page's alarm, he found the entrance to be a winding channel little more than ten feet deep. Since the *Water Witch* drew nine feet of water, constant depth soundings were necessary. Still, they were able to reach the harbor at Montevideo, Uruguay, by midnight, guided by a revolving beacon on shore.

From there they moved on to Buenos Aires, one hundred miles up the river on the Argentine shore. Now came four long months of regular naval duties before the actual expedition could begin. Palmer continued his medical duties, but spent as much time as possible fulfilling a special assignment from the Smithsonian Institution: the collection of seeds and living plants that might be grown in the United States. He was able to send at least one package back to the States aboard a returning merchant schooner before the *Water Witch* started upriver for Paraguay on August 31, 1853.

By daylight the La Plata was a sea of red soup from tons of silt washed down off the pampas, the prairies of South America. Palmer heard there was a deposit of mud thirty feet deep on its bottom. He did not doubt it after witnessing a sudden *pampero* which blew the entire river out of sight for hours, leaving ships aground on red mud flats stretching to the horizon.

One of the principal duties of the expedition was to measure and chart a practical channel for ocean-going vessels up the La Plata, Paraná, and Paraguay rivers. Few accurate maps of this La Plata system were available. Any nation possessing one had a distinct trade advantage over all its competitors. The *Water Witch*'s officers spent a great deal of time on this project. In addition, Page hired pilots at various river ports along the way from time to time to provide knowledge of local conditions.

An elevated section of the hurricane deck was used for the necessary observations. Compass, chronometer, and sextant readings helped to establish their exact position. The lead was lowered every five minutes in deep water and oftener in shallow water to determine channel depth. One man would project the course on a map, showing the width and depth of the river and the principal features of either bank. Another would record the details in a notebook.

Palmer spent the daylight hours on deck in a transfixed stare at the closest shore. He yearned mightily for something to happen that would cause them to land, so he might go ashore to collect from the wonderful tangle of wild flowers that nearly smothered every inch of visible land.

The entrance to the Paraná River in Argentina was a maze of islands covered with a growth that awed even the most seasoned of the sailors. Forests of wild peach and orange trees thronged to the water's edge. Graceful willows arched the narrow channels between islands. Blossoming tropical vines and air plants studded every tree with floral jewels. All were new to Palmer. The Argentine pilot pointed out strange ones like the ceibo tree with its glistening foliage and pink blooms that turned deep purple. This was the tree that the jaguar was supposed to scratch whenever he felt his claws burn.

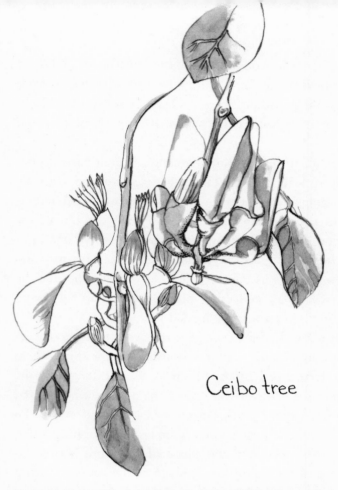

Ceibo tree

Its bark was also good for dyeing wool and excellent for curing a jaguar bite, the pilot added.

Palmer seldom viewed the left bank of the Paraná. It was out of sight across this giant of a river — more than twelve miles wide in many places. The channel lay closer to the right bank. Nevertheless, when Palmer climbed the steamer's sixty-foot mast, he viewed nothing but a wilderness of water and tropical foliage. As far as he could see were wooded islands and river with clouds of water birds rising in alarm at the *chunk-chunk* of their approaching paddle wheel. Geese, ducks, and black-necked swans were everywhere. If only the ship would stop!

She did, at the town of Diamante, Argentina, but only briefly to load fuel. Captain Page had arranged with the Argentine government to have stacks of wood left at various points along the way. Collecting was out of the question, for the riverbank here rose to nearly one hundred feet. Not until they reached La Paz, Argentina, on September 14 was Palmer able to leave the ship. Here he had a field day collecting plants under Captain Page's direction while the crew loaded fuel.

Just out of La Paz, Page gave the order that the officers might hunt and the crew might fish from the ship to help supply fresh provisions. Much as Palmer longed to be the only collector, it was one of the officers who bagged their first prize, a magnificent black-necked swan. To Palmer fell the rather unpleasant task of skinning it for a specimen. Yet even this phase of collecting seemed as thrilling to the young Englishman as the actual securing of the specimen. He prepared the skin with precision as Dr. Kirtland had taught him. He packed it with care, that it might reach Washington in first-class order.

The next day two capybaras appeared on the riverbank and the officers again brought them down with carbines. The huge male weighed one hundred pounds and the female, ninety-one. These largest rodents on earth looked for all the world like giant guinea pigs. Palmer had watched them feeding on vegetation along the shore, ready to dive underwater at the slightest alarm. Once again, it was his job to skin them for specimens.

Continuing up the Paraná, the men looked up to see an enormous black cloud rapidly coming their way. The captain trained his telescope on it and announced it to be a swarm of migrating locusts. Soon a mass of insects swirled through the air around the *Water Witch*, catching in her rigging and falling to the deck in buzzing heaps. Most of the crew retreated below decks, but Palmer remained above to observe the strange occurrence in complete fascination. He quickly gathered up a box of locusts before they could be cleared away.

Every mile of their ascent to Paraguay was filled with such events, much to Palmer's delight. One day they sighted a red deer swimming across the river, and took to a lifeboat to chase it down and capture it alive. Another night they went fishing for "jumping mullet" in their small boat. By rapping on its sides they made the fish leap wildly from the water and into the boat.

Then, near Tobaco Island, the *Water Witch* had her first of many breakdowns. The muddy river water was such a strain on her wheel that she broke a crank strap. While awaiting repairs, Captain Page took Palmer ashore to collect. They shot four monkeys and a *ciconia*, an enormous black and white stork with a startling red, black, and yellow bill.

Corrientes was the last Argentine town on the Paraná River before the expedition entered the Paraguay River, which bordered Paraguay on the southwest. While the *Water Witch* took on fuel, Palmer went ashore again, armed with a botanical portfolio and seed bag for plant collecting. Accompanying him this time was a daguerreotype artist, one of the officers skilled in this early form of photography. The captain had instructed him to take pictures of the most interesting of the trees and flowers.

There on the shallow lagoons near Corrientes they first discovered the most gorgeous of all water lilies, the *Victoria regia*. Its magnificent blooms opened pure white with pink rims which later spread and deepened to red. Even more outstanding were its leaves: immense copper-green platters a yard across. Here also they noticed the *camilote*, a species of water lily which floated with the current and was a sign of falling water in the upper Paraguay River, according to the pilot. The season of floods and high water was past, and Captain Page was worried that the *Water Witch* might not be able to cross all of Paraguay if the water level dropped too low.

They hurried on. Three miles above Corrientes was Guardia Cerito, the first of Paraguay's military posts. They were to encounter these outposts every three miles, for Paraguay was the best-armed country in South America. Up to this moment Captain Page had not fired his guns in the traditional military salute, for fear of damaging his precious chronometers. But now, realizing that the success of his work in Paraguay might depend upon how well he observed diplomatic courtesy, he fired a thirteen-gun salute.

They were waved on toward Asunción, the capital city. Now the character of the land changed. Gone were the chains of forested islands of the Paraná. In-

Water lilies,
  Victoria regia
    camilote

stead, the banks of the Paraguay were like well-kept lawns filled with tall palm trees. These were soon replaced by fields of corn, tobacco, and *mandioca*, or cassava, the closer they came to Asunción.

On October 1, 1853, the *Water Witch* finally steamed into the anchorage at Asunción, capital of Paraguay. Again she fired salutes, which were promptly answered by the field pieces in front of the Government House. Then began a month-long stay while Captain Page conferred with President López concerning a trade agreement and further exploration up the Paraguay River.

Palmer used his free time to explore the town. It was a botanist's paradise. Purple bougainvillea climbed adobe walls. Flaming poinsettias fringed patios. Scarlet flame trees lined cobblestone streets. Every garden was a riot of jasmine, hibiscus, and roses. Tangerine and orange groves bordered the city. Palms and tropical hardwoods stretched to the sky. Across the river lay the vast mysterious Chaco, a low-lying jungle full of wild tribes and strange trees.

Palmer soon found himself collecting more than plants. For every flower, tree, or shrub around Asunción, there seemed to be a folk tale describing its special powers. The seeds of the *macagua* tree would cure snake bites, people said. This they knew because the *macagua* bird, which lived on snakes, always ate the tree's seeds whenever it was bitten. Powder from the roots of the *ayui* (laurel) would dissolve gallstones. When burned, its incense gave protection from epidemics. Resin from the *cabera* was good for curing toothaches. Sap from the *ibira paye* would cure anything. Palmer began filling his notebook with such curious items.

Everyone Palmer met seemed well acquainted with every tree and flower in Asunción. These people actually loved and appreciated plants the way he did. He was soon to learn why.

After a week in Asunción, Dr. Carter declared there was not one true medical man in all of Paraguay. Sick people in towns like Asunción turned to men called *curanderos*, he had learned. These were merely self-trained dealers in plant remedies. Country families depended entirely upon their own knowledge in using wild plants for medicines.

Purely by chance, Edward Palmer had stumbled upon one of the world's most highly developed folk-medicine practices. He was greatly impressed. Then and there he began a careful study of such plant uses, an interest which would remain with him the rest of his life.

On November 7 at 5:30 A.M., the *Water Witch* steamed out of Asunción, bound north across Paraguay as far as a deep channel would take them. President López had, indeed, been fussy about diplomatic courtesy, but otherwise had seemed friendly enough. He had readily given permission for further exploration and had passed the word on to the upriver forts. Page felt confident enough to leave behind one of his officers to direct the building of a second smaller boat for investigating the Paraguay's shallower tributaries.

For Palmer the second half of the journey proved as exciting as the first. They caught a tapir, although its mate escaped when their shot bounced harmlessly off its tough hide. They captured a seven-foot boa constrictor, which gave Palmer no end of trouble getting its thick coils into the preserving alcohol. They met a wild Indian band riding bareback among the palms on the riverbank. Captain Page gave them gifts of tobacco and beads for which they promised to return with animal skins, but they were never heard from again. The crank shaft broke four times, giving Palmer added opportunity to collect plants.

Months before, Captain Page had obtained Brazil's permission to explore her portion of the Paraguay River as far north as Corumbá. Now, as he reached Paraguay's northern border, he directed the steamer into Brazil without hesitation. But rapidly falling water on the upper river soon started them back toward Asunción. At Fort Coimbra, Brazil's last settlement above the Paraguayan border, they went ashore at the *comandante's* invitation to explore the famous cave, Grotto Inferno. Palmer gazed in awe at the immense limestone cavern as the men's torches lit giant stalactites with a thousand sparkling jewels. When they returned to the ship, a 250-pound sample of one of these limestone icicles accompanied them.

Returning through Paraguay, the *Water Witch* began to encounter a rather cool reception at forts and settlements that had welcomed her openly only a few weeks before. Page could not understand it. When they finally reached Asunción the reason became all too clear. They had violated López's trust by crossing into Brazil. Soon Captain Page himself became embroiled in the bewildering politics of Paraguay. Yet when the *Water Witch* began her return trip down to Montevideo, Uruguay, on January 30, 1854, relations with López seemed as friendly as ever.

Palmer's second year in South America was decidedly disappointing. He was assigned to the ship for the entire year, with few opportunities for collecting. Meanwhile, Captain Page and half the crew went exploring the Paraná's tributaries in Argentina on their new little vessel built at Asunción, the *Pilcomayo*.

Worse still, the fall of 1854 brought a more serious difficulty: malaria. Palmer was one of the first to be stricken. His early attacks were brief, with hardly a hint of the grim fever which would plague him the rest of his life.

On January 31, 1855, the *Water Witch* left Corrientes, Argentina, for a routine run up the Paraná River to Paraguay to survey a certain rapids. Lieutenant Jeffers was in charge, with an Argentine pilot guiding the vessel through the winding channel. As they approached Paraguay, the pilot kept them close to the Argentine shore and as far as possible from Fort Itapirú on the Paraguay side. Without warning, the vessel suddenly ran aground on a sand bar. At this, a small boat was dispatched from the fort to the ship with a message for Captain Page. Since he was not aboard, and since Lieutenant Jeffers could not read Spanish, the message was sent back unanswered. It was to inform them that Paraguay's waters were now closed to foreign warships.

Unaware of this development, Lieutenant Jeffers freed the *Water Witch* and once more began his ascent of the

Paraná River, this time closer to the fort to avoid the sand bar. Suddenly a warning volley rang out from the fort. Then real shot poured into the American vessel, cutting away the tiller and killing the helmsman. Surprise gave way to anger when the sailors realized they were being shelled. Palmer found himself in charge of bringing up ammunition from the ship's magazine as the *Water Witch* returned fire. The skirmish was a short one, but long enough to give Edward Palmer his first taste of dressing gunshot wounds and attending to the dead.

Without her tiller for maneuvering, the *Water Witch* was forced to retreat back to Corrientes. When Captain Page learned what had happened, he protested the incident vigorously but futilely to López. It would be many years before America's one-day war with Paraguay was fully resolved.

Meanwhile, Palmer's malaria recurred, and when the expedition returned to Montevideo, Uruguay, in February he went ashore for good. The attack was serious and left him so weak that he asked to be discharged from the expedition. While the *Water Witch* proceeded back to the Paraná for several more months of exploring, Palmer remained in Montevideo until April, when he was able to secure passage back to Washington on a trading schooner.

Instead of resting and recuperating in Montevideo, he spent his long days of waiting in the pursuit of his newfound love: collecting. He caught fish, captured snakes, gathered insects, and pressed plants all on his own, to be carried back with him to Washington's great museum, the Smithsonian Institution.

Palmer's La Plata experiences were to last him a lifetime, not as fond memories, but as the clear-cut chart of his life's work for the next fifty-five years. Even before his schooner landed he had penned the following letter to the secretary of the Smithsonian:

Washington City, June 13th-1855

Dear Sir

I beg to lay before you an application for an appointment in any expedition that may be formed.

I have just returned from the Exploriseing expedition to the Laplat River and the success which have attended my labours may be judged from the quality of the specimens collected. In the preservation of birds-insects-fish quadrupeds and botanical specimens I take great interest.

Intending to spend my life in the prosecution of science and trusting my qualifications be found sufficient to meet with your favourable consideration.

I remain, your obedient survent

Edward Palmer

(From Smithsonian Archives, Letters Received, Book 71)

4

Overland

He couldn't believe it. He just could not believe that the Smithsonian Institution had no openings for an experienced collector like himself. Already Palmer had a high regard for his abilities. He was proud of the job he had performed in Paraguay. Surely others must feel the same. It never occurred to him that in the eyes of the navy, he had been a very minor member of the La Plata expedition. What a shock when the account of it came out without any mention of his name! What an omen of things to come!

There was nothing to do but return to Cleveland. His friends would be anxious to hear of his adventures. Dr. Kirtland and Speaker Taylor welcomed him with open arms and a flood of questions. But after he had told his story — over and over — what then? Palmer felt a great emptiness, the depressing letdown so familiar to travelers who have just completed an exciting journey and must now settle down to humdrum living. It was a feeling he did not like.

Yet instead of brooding about it, he lost himself among Dr. Kirtland's natural history and medical books. He even attempted a bit of collecting — some grasshoppers — but tame Cleveland was no Paraguay. In September 1855 he tried the Smithsonian again. Still there were no expeditions with an opening for a young plant collector.

By now the urge to travel was much too strong for Palmer to resist. Where to go? His only definite offer had come from his mother in England. Her letters were forever urging him to return, and lately she had mentioned news of a great exhibition at the Crystal Palace in London. Yes, it would be nice to visit his old homeland.

The more he thought about it, the more convinced he became that it was just the thing to do. He would not be returning for good; just for a visit. His plant collecting could wait for a few months. There was never a doubt in his mind but that he would eventually land a position as a plant collector. While he was marking time, he might just as well be traveling.

Once his plans were made, Palmer as usual put them into action without delay. Even before the month was out, he was bound once again across the Atlantic.

The great distance involved, the time, the money — none of these seemed to bother Edward Palmer once his decision to travel was made. But this time, the details of the trip remain vague. Only his occasional letters to Professor Spencer Baird, assistant secretary of the Smithsonian Institution, provide any hint at all as to what must have happened.

In the six years he had been away, many changes had taken place in Wilton village, especially among its residents. All of his immediate friends were gone. Many of the young adults he now met had been children when he first left for America. He felt like a stranger in his own home town — but was a handsome and intriguing stranger so far as the girls were concerned.

One young woman of nineteen, Dinah Riches by name, found him especially so. Her intense interest in everything Palmer had done during the past six years was enough to overcome even his unusual shyness toward girls. Before he knew what was happening to him, Edward Palmer was in love.

But he had grave doubts. Would this lovely young lady actually give up her family and homeland to return to America with him? Did such a refined and delicate girl want to share the rough life of a plant collector? That Dinah would and did hardly seemed possible to Palmer. Nevertheless, they were married March 29, 1856, spent their honeymoon in London, and set out across the Atlantic on April 16.

Their ship was the great *Amazon*, one of the new and splendid sailing packets on the North Atlantic run. Captain Henry Hovey announced at the outset that they were trying for a new speed record to New York, a crossing of fourteen days or less.

Dinah had never seen such elegance. The Atlantic sailing liners of the 1850s were floating palaces with elaborately lighted staterooms and magnificent main cabins finished in rosewood and mahogany. For first- and second-class passengers there was the unheard-of luxury of a shower bath — that is, if the travelers did not mind salt water dipped from the ocean.

But the voyage itself soon dampened the spirits of the newlyweds. Less than one day out of Liverpool, a furious wind sprang up, whipping the sea into mountainous waves. Most of the women and many of the men took to their beds for the remainder of the crossing, completely overcome with seasickness. All thoughts of a new speed record were quickly put aside. Every effort of captain and crew was focused instead on reaching New York safely.

If Palmer had been the worrying kind, he might have thought twice before attempting his return voyage at this time. The year of 1856 had thus far been the stormiest, most violent one on record. First the *Ocean Queen* had gone down early in the year with all hands. Then the great steamship *Pacific* had disappeared without a trace just outside of Liverpool, with 285 passengers aboard.

As if in sympathy with the sea's violent mood, life itself seemed filled with black days in 1856. A great depression gripped the world. Terrible plagues spread throughout many lands. Rumors of ruin and failure cropped up everywhere. Even New York was in the throes of a yellow fever epidemic when the *Amazon* docked.

Soon after Palmer carried his seasick wife ashore, his letters to his friends, relatives, and acquaintances abruptly stopped. We can only guess at the tragedy that must have overwhelmed him. His young bride, weakened by endless days of seasickness, caught yellow fever and died. Her death hurt Palmer beyond words, for never again did he mention Dinah to a living soul.

Cleveland, Ohio, was still his only home in America, and it was there Palmer returned early in the summer. Still in the depths of black despair, the twenty-five-year-old collector realized that life must go on and he must find a way to support himself. Professor Baird's replies to his letters were polite, even friendly, but contained no job offers for a plant collector.

What to do? It seemed almost natural that he should turn to medicine. He had great admiration for Dr. Kirtland, one of the top medical men of the day. Moreover, he had been a hospital steward on the *Water Witch* for two years. He had also developed a great interest in using plant remedies to cure disease. Perhaps, even his wife's death spurred him on to learn more about sicknesses and their cures. His taxidermist's skill in preparing animal specimens gave him an excellent background in anatomy. The Latin which he already knew from plant names was also the language of medicine. Yes, he could easily earn his living as a doctor. He began attending lectures in medicine at the Cleveland Homeopathic College.

To graduate, he would need three years of study in a medical office plus two courses of lectures at the college. He had no intention of spending that much time learning a profession in which he already felt sufficiently skilled. Medical training in Palmer's day was still in its infancy. Many doctors completed the required courses and earned their degrees, it is true. But just as many called themselves "doctor" on their own initiative when they felt they were ready to practice. Although such "doctors" might have had trouble finding positions in the advanced eastern cities, dozen of western settlements were clamoring for their services.

After six months of college lectures in Cleveland, Edward Palmer felt quite ready to begin his new career. He took the title of "doctor" and turned his face west.

To go somewhere, anywhere new and different, was again uppermost in his thoughts. He began by following the great river highways of 1857: down the Ohio to the Mississippi; up the Mississippi to the Missouri; up the Missouri to the Great Western Bend country along the Kansas-Missouri border. This was the very border not long before declared "America's permanent frontier." Beyond it lay nothing but Indian country and the "Great American Desert," as everything west of Missouri was called.

Yet long before Palmer's arrival, pioneers and forty-niners had pushed off from here for the long trek west. The Santa Fe and Oregon Trails began at Independence, Missouri, now part of Kansas City. The Holladay Overland Mail and the Butterfield Overland Despatch soon would be operating out of Atchison, Kansas. Outfitting centers now lined the river, and farmers were beginning to cross over into once forbidding prairie lands.

Not only was the border abuzz with emigrants when Palmer arrived in 1857; it was abroil with slavery trouble. Proslavery gangs from Missouri staged frequent raids into Kansas. Antislavery "free-soilers" from the North were shipped in by the boatload to meet them head on. Despite such unsettled conditions, Palmer could not have been more pleased with his surroundings. He spent his first year in Highland, Kansas, and his second near Leavenworth. Doctoring was almost abandoned while he poked around the wonderful rolling hills or packed out onto the prairies, collecting natural history material.

Whenever he had a boxful, he would ship it off to Professor Baird at the Smithsonian. But whatever his plans for the future may have been — whether or not he was still waiting for an expedition opening — everything was suddenly swept aside by that soul-piercing shout echoing out of the Colorado mountains: Gold!

Not that Edward Palmer wanted any. Money never held much meaning in his life. Just enough to keep him going was all he ever asked for — or got. No, the Colorado mountain call rang with a different sound in his ears. The gold he dreamed of shimmered in the leaves of the quaking aspen and glowed in the petals of the evening primrose high in the mountain meadows.

By spring of 1859 Leavenworth was bursting with fortune hunters bound west. Some say more than 100,000 people crossed the Nebraska trails that year with their wagon signs shouting, "Pikes Peak or Bust!" Nobody knows how many slogged back a year later with nothing left but their sense of humor: "Busted, b'Gosh!"

Palmer hitched a ride with the first group. No doubt they felt quite lucky to have a doctor aboard, until they realized his passion lay with picking flowers, not mending bones. At every stop, he collected and pressed plants until his pack was bulging.

The Kansas towns Palmer knew had been raw and unruly, but they were peaceful country hamlets compared to Colorado's mining camps. Golden, Black Hawk, Central City, and Empire sprang up overnight from mushrooming tent towns. Log cabins with sawdust floors and gunny-sack carpets replaced tents the second season. Unpainted shanties began to line the wheel ruts as soon as a sawmill moved in. Streets were filthy, food was scarce, and water (flavored with citric acid to disguise its sickening taste) was peddled in the streets for ten cents a bucket.

Palmer settled in the center of it all: the bustling village of Denver City. As usual he ignored the rip-roaring life around him and proceeded on his collecting trips into the mountains. While the *Rocky Mountain News* carried such items as this: "We are curious to know how long this reckless and promiscuous firing of pistols, cutting and stabbing will be permitted . . ." Palmer's notes sounded quite different:

6 miles up in the mountains & 14 from Denver City
Col. Teritory

No. 1.   Larkspur, bronzey blue petal, dark purple
         calax bronzey mouth yellowish white striped
         blueish purple. Grown upon rich hill slopes
         June 11-1861
No. 2)   Only grows upon range of mts blooms from May
         to June
No 2)   Same as (No 2), but pink, rare very . . .
(From Smithsonian Institution, Accession 291)

These were a part of the field notes meant to accompany the 165 specimens he collected that season. Not every plant was named, of course, for many were new or unknown to him. It was up to the experts at the Smithsonian to identify and name them.

Then began the tedious, but to him fascinating, part of collecting, that of preparing the specimens. Each plant had to be flattened in a plant press between blotters which were changed frequently to insure proper drying. The plants were then separately mounted on heavy white paper, labeled, and packed for shipment.

His excitement over the collection can only be imagined. It was far more precious to him than gold. How many plants were new to science? Would any be named perhaps for him? But the quirk of fate that seemed to have plagued Edward Palmer from the beginning was at work again. The box he finally sent off by stagecoach became lost en route and did not arrive at the Smithsonian until three long years later, much of its value gone by that time. As for the field notes, they arrived separately in 1862, only to be filed away and lost until 1943!

With the opening of a transcontinental stagecoach line in early summer, Denver suddenly found itself linked with California and the rest of the West. It proved too much for Palmer to resist. By August he was ready to board the Holladay Overland Mail for the three-week trip to San Francisco.

For a frail man like Palmer, the journey must have been torture. Jolting over primitive roads made sleep nearly impossible in a coach full of passengers. Roasted by sun, soaked by spattering rain, but mostly suffocated by the everlasting dust, they were thankful to pile out at the home stations every fifty miles. At these crude log huts, the drivers and stock were changed and meals were served. A dollar fifty was the charge for a cut of rancid bacon, a chunk of maggoty bread, and a mug of "dishwater" coffee. Many complained that the horses were treated better than the passengers on the early lines.

But his view of the wondrous West was worth it all. Through the magnificent Rockies . . . over to spic-and-span Salt Lake City . . . across the sagebrush-dotted basins of Nevada . . . down into the dreaded dry "sinks" with "dust-devils," those midget whirlwinds of the hot Southwest, swirling about them. Then up through the high Sierras . . . over breathtaking Donner Pass . . . and finally down to Hangtown, California, where the wilted passengers had their first chance to wash.

In California, Palmer's knowledge of natural history stood him in good stead for the first time. He landed a job with the State Geological Survey and was sent to San Diego to collect sea animals for three months. One of his superiors found him so industrious that he named a new shell *Tritonia palmeri* in his honor.

Palmer might have remained there for some time, had not history given him a nudge. War had broken out between the North and the South the previous spring. He had heard its reasons argued long ago in the Cleveland parlors of Speaker Taylor. He had seen its bloody rumblings on the Kansas border. Now he heard the call for Union volunteers — and heeded it.

5

War Whoop

Wartime Washington was a hive of activity. Palmer had come the long way around to reach it. Instead of another jolting stagecoach trip back across the continent, he had chosen a speedier journey by steamer down to Panama, where he crossed the Isthmus and caught a second ship to New York.

From there he proceeded directly to Washington. By good fortune, the first recruiting officer he met was Colonel Jesse H. Leavenworth, son of the famous frontier general for whom Fort Leavenworth had been named. Colonel Leavenworth was just then bound for Denver, Colorado, to raise a cavalry regiment. He promised Palmer an appointment as assistant surgeon in the Second Colorado Regiment if he would come along. Palmer was only too happy to accept. His four years in the West had made him eager to see more of this exciting land.

Back across the country Palmer trekked, stopping at Leavenworth, Kansas, where the regiment gathered, and finally parading in triumph down the main street of Denver on June 2, 1862, just ten months from the time of his last visit. The tired column with its huge supply train stretched out for half a mile. But one trooper could smile through his weariness. Dr. Edward Palmer had a load of new plants in his pack, a choice collection that traced the long march from Kansas.

But his peaceful collecting days were short-lived. The Indian troubles which had brought the regiment west soon called for his full attention. He was stationed at Camp Weld outside Denver, but spent most of his time on the trail with the troops. Into the mountains to enforce the law . . . down to Fort Lyons to settle Indian troubles on the Platte . . . over to Fort Larned, Kansas, twelve days away . . . back to Fort Lyons again to "overhaul" the hospital.

Then in May 1863, with a long march back to Fort Scott on the Kansas-Missouri border, the real war began for Palmer. This was the land of the Five Civilized Tribes. The Cherokees, Creeks, Seminoles, Choctaws, and Chickasaws were "tame" Indians, brought from the southern states years before by the federal government and resettled near here on the empty prairies. They had their own governments, farms, and schools, and even their own Negro slaves before the war broke out.

The southern whites in Kansas and Oklahoma were quick to enlist their aid against the Union. Under their own Cherokee general, Stand Watie, bands of Confederate Indian troops soon turned the territory into a bloody battlefield. Crops were burned, settlements and stock destroyed. Overland travel to the West came to a virtual halt.

Then the Union entered the fray with its own civilized Indian allies, as well as freed Negro slaves and western cavalry units like Palmer's. Fort Scott in Kansas was their stronghold, and Confederate Fort Smith in Arkansas their objective.

Palmer rode most of the way to Fort Scott in an ambulance with the sick. Still, he was able to collect a few plants whenever they stopped. These, along with his Colorado specimens, he sent to Professor Baird at his first opportunity.

All of this time Palmer had been patiently awaiting his formal appointment in the army. Colonel Leavenworth was evidently too busy to act on a vague promise made long ago in Washington. Palmer's complaints got him nowhere. Yet no appointment meant no pay, and when his money ran out he was forced to take some kind of action. A personal appeal directly to the Secretary of War finally solved his problem. Although it was not the appointment he had hoped for, Palmer was nevertheless enlisted as a private in the Second Colorado Volunteer Cavalry by order of the War Department. After twenty long months of army service, he finally received all of his back pay.

A photograph taken at the time shows Palmer in his army uniform as a smallish man of thirty-two, still darkly handsome with his trim beard and drooping mustache in the style of the day. His army papers describe him as five feet, six inches tall, with black hair and brown eyes, and by occupation — not doctor, but "nurseryman."

Palmer was all doctor on the June morning he accompanied a large supply train south. His regiment was to make certain the two hundred wagons arrived safely at starving Fort Gibson in the Cherokee Nation. Confederate Indians had all but cut off this distant outpost with their successful attacks on every wagon train. Now even the weather seemed to be against the Federal forces.

Unceasing rains had flooded every creek and river along the way. Still they pushed on. Twenty friendly Cherokee scouts led the way. Then unexpectedly, the scouts spotted a fresh trail made by Stand Watie's advance pickets. Now they knew a surprise attack was in the making. But the Union troops had been warned. With the silent swiftness of tigers stalking their prey, the Union Indians tracked down and destroyed Watie's scouts.

The next day at Cabin Creek it was Union troops that surprised 1,500 Confederate Indians lying in wait on either side of the swollen stream. For half an hour mountain howitzers boomed and Minié balls whistled, destroying the bridge and scattering the Rebel troops on the near side of the creek.

Across the rampaging stream, the remaining Rebels looked on helplessly, unable to cross over and help their comrades. The following day, as the waters receded, five companies of Negro troops and a regiment of Indians advanced across the creek to defeat them. Only three Union soldiers were killed, thirty were wounded, and nine enemy prisoners were taken. It was Palmer's first full-scale battle and the Rebels' last attempt to stop a Union supply train in the West.

Three days later Palmer and the troops arrived at Fort Gibson for the summer. Their mission was not only to defend this outpost but to launch a Federal drive against the Confederate stronghold, Fort Smith in Arkansas. Guessing this, the Rebel forces began their own surprise march on Fort Gibson to catch the Federals off guard. But the Union troops were one step ahead. An all-night march took them to Honey Springs on the Texas Road where the Rebels were encamped. The clash that followed soon became a wholesale Rebel rout, the turning point of the Civil War in the West. With the ragged Indians retreating down the Texas Road went the last hopes of the South. Six weeks later Palmer's regiment occupied Fort Smith.

The return march to St. Louis, Missouri, in midwinter was anything but victorious for Palmer. He almost did not make it. Exposure to the harsh weather plus the return of fever weakened him so much he was unable to follow his unit back into the field. Nevertheless, as long as he was on his feet he continued to do his job. He remained behind in the field hospital at Pleasant Hill, Missouri, as steward in charge of casualties.

In March an order came through from Kansas City requesting his help in the hospital there. But work was slack in April, and somehow Palmer managed to spend his leave on a hasty trip to Washington, D.C. He had heard it rumored that a scientific expedition to Minnesota was being planned. Nothing came of it, however, and May found him back in Kansas City.

This time his ever delicate health gave way so completely that he found himself a patient. After several months in and out of bed, Palmer received an army discharge declaring him disabled from "rheumatism and heart disease." But the army had written off the determined young doctor much too soon. In three months' time he was back as a civilian contract surgeon in charge of wounded Confederate prisoners in the Kansas City General Hospital. And six months later he began a journey which would end in military duty more risky than any he had ever known.

6

Arizona Plants

Palmer's last month in Kansas City was a whirl of hospital duties and trip preparations. The war was over and he was free once more to go where he pleased. He had met a group of southwesterners preparing to return to the new Territory of Arizona. Their talk soon rekindled his memories of the Far West, and they had no trouble convincing him to come along. What a collector's paradise such an untouched land was sure to be!

But things were different this trip. The white man's war fever had spread to the Plains Indians. The postwar West was a sputtering powder keg ready to explode. Everywhere along the way Palmer had to be reminded of the danger and urged to stay close to the main party. Even at Fort Whipple, Arizona's year-old capital, he was forced to tag along with the cavalry whenever he wanted to collect.

But he was not alone in his excitement over Arizona's strange new plants and animals. For the first time in his life, Edward Palmer met another man like himself. Elliott Coues, the fort's doctor, was ten years younger than Palmer, but already an active collector. That he would soon become a nationally known scientist and author, Palmer had no hint.

All Palmer saw that spring evening of his arrival was a smiling young officer of twenty-three, looking even younger with his clean-shaven face. (Beards and mustaches were the rule among most frontier troopers.) Coues was delighted to welcome a fellow naturalist after months at the fort with no one who shared his interests. Always open and talkative, he could hardly wait to tell Palmer about the wonderful collecting opportunities.

But Palmer eyed Coues with suspicion. After all, who was this strange young fellow exploring the new land ahead of him? He claimed to know Professor Baird. He talked about an expedition he had accompanied to Labrador. He spoke with authority on all phases of natural history — but mostly about birds, to Palmer's great relief. Palmer relaxed a bit when he learned that the new plants of Arizona were still his to discover.

Yet it was not easy for Palmer to unbend. He had always followed science on his own. He had always kept his own counsel. Now suddenly he was confronted with someone exactly like himself, someone alert, curious, and totally absorbed in the fascinating natural world around him.

But there was a difference. Coues had graduated from college at the age of seventeen. By nineteen he had earned his doctor's degree, published seven scholarly papers, and accompanied a scientific expedition to Labrador. His present assignment as an army officer and full-fledged M.D. included scientific collecting under orders from Professor Baird. At twenty-three he was already well on his way to becoming one of nineteenth-century America's greatest naturalists.

And then, there was the man himself. Where Palmer was shy and reserved, Coues was a brilliant conversationalist. Where Palmer was ever the serious, solitary field worker, Coues joked and laughed with the men, and soon had them out chasing lizards, snakes, and butterflies for his collections.

Yet Palmer and Coues got on well enough at first. Palmer spent every waking hour collecting plants around the fort and along the trails. Coues used every minute he could spare away from his dispensary to gather birds and animals and even a few plants. They collected together whenever they could — but perhaps for protection as much as companionship.

A shrubby hillside near the fort was Coues's favorite spot, not for the number of birds he found, but for the lack of Indians! The bloody Indian fighting would forever color his memories of Arizona's birds. Under one mesquite tree, where a tiny yellow-headed verdin flitted, lay a dead trooper with an arrow in his back. In a ravine where a bold little canyon wren had led him lay several naked and still bleeding soldiers ambushed by the Apaches. Such scenes would haunt him forever.

Apache trouble had brought the troopers to the new territory in the first place. But instead of bringing peace, the presence of the soldiers seemed to spark new Apache attacks. Coues was ordered to stay within shouting distance of the fort. Even so, he examined every bush and shrub for lurking savages before looking for birds.

Palmer mentioned the danger in his journal, but as usual ignored it in his eagerness to collect the strange new plants. Like Coues, he too was restricted to the fort environs and allowed to collect in the field only when the cavalry rode out on a scout. The fort commander would never understand why men like Palmer and Coues were willing to risk their lives over a new plant or bird. Only a man possessed by the same scientific zeal and curiosity could explain how all else was forgotten whenever an unknown specimen appeared.

The two collectors were certainly rivals, yet there is no evidence they considered each other as such. It is more probable that neither took the other very seriously. Palmer was ten years older. He surely considered his many years of collecting and medical experience as far superior to Coues's training. No doubt he looked upon the younger man as an eager but unseasoned youth.

Coues, on the other hand, saw himself as the expert assigned by the Smithsonian to collect wildlife specimens on the western frontier. To him Palmer was probably an outsider of little consequence, just a private collector and self-proclaimed doctor having no official connection with any scientific institution. However, he would gladly carry Palmer's plant collection east with him when he left for Washington at the end of the summer, as Palmer requested.

Coues dropped off Palmer's plants along with some of

his own at the St. Louis offices of Dr. George Engelmann. Engelmann was by far the most respected botanist west of the Mississippi. He had already become one of the greatest authorities on western plants, especially cactuses. His Missouri Botanical Garden was world-famous, as well. Collections of western plants such as Coues's and Palmer's were frequently sent to him to identify, either directly by the collector or by institutions like the Smithsonian.

His was an exacting yet fascinating task: examining each plant to determine its identity. With his vast storehouse of knowledge, he could tell at a glance to which plant family a new specimen belonged. Then he would look for its genus, the next step down the orderly ladder of classification, and finally for its species or specific name. Each plant was always identified by two Latin names: the first for its special group (genus) and the second for its distinctive characteristics within that special group (species). Engelmann's name would then follow these terms, so that botanists throughout the world would know who had identified the plant.

For instance, one specimen he later received from Arizona consisted of a leaf, a nut, and a catkin (a tree's flower-spike). The texture of the leaf quickly told Engelmann it belonged to the family *Fagaceae*. There are several genera in this family, the most important being oak, beech, and chestnut. When Engelmann saw that the nut was an acorn, not a spiny burr, and that the catkin was drooping, not erect, he knew it belonged to the oak genus, *Quercus*.

Next he went to his herbarium to compare this *Quer-*

cus with all the others on file. Here were hundreds of plants, each mounted flat on a sheet of strong white paper within heavy folders called "covers." Nuts and cones were kept in labeled boxes. Soft fruits were stored in liquid. This oak was different from any in his collection, so Engelmann turned to his library to search through all of the literature published on the genus *Quercus.*

It was soon evident that here indeed was a new species. Had there been any question, he would have consulted other experts in the field. Its genus name, *Quercus,* having been determined, it was now up to Engelmann to choose the specific name. According to the rules of nomenclature, he could use any Latin word not already applied to the genus *Quercus.* He could not name the tree for himself, but he might use the Latin form of the collector's name, or that of a fellow botanist or of the place where the tree had been discovered, or even a descriptive term for the tree itself. He chose to call this new Arizona oak *Quercus palmeri,* the Palmer oak.

The specimen was then preserved as a "type," and a description of it published. This name could never be changed unless it later turned out that someone else had previously identified the tree — or if it should prove to be merely a variety of some already-named oak species. This was not the case with the Palmer oak, and it still remains one of the distinctive scrub-oak species of the Arizona highlands.

Palmer was not a trained botanist, nor a "taxonomist," as these identification specialists were called. He gladly left the sorting and naming of his specimens up to men such as Engelmann in St. Louis; Asa Gray at Harvard

Beargrass

College, America's greatest nineteenth-century botanist; John Torrey at Columbia College; and the various experts in Washington.

How impatiently he must have waited, in those days of poor communications, to hear the results of his first Arizona collection! The news, when it finally arrived more than a year later, was incredible. Coues had betrayed him! He had taken all the credit himself for the entire collection.

The truth of the matter will probably never be known. It is doubtful that Coues purposely gave Engelmann the impression he was the sole collector. Honesty was high on Coues's list of virtues. Moreover, plants never meant that much to him. More likely he felt it was unimportant to emphasize the part played by an unknown, untrained collector like Palmer.

But when Palmer learned that all of his hard-won plants were labeled with Coues's name, he was beside himself. The endless days he had spent gathering them at the risk of his life . . . the long nights he had devoted to pressing them at the peril of his ever frail health! His letters of protest flooded the scientific world. But the best he could ever do about the mistake was to have his own name added. Many of Palmer's early Arizona plants are still tagged: "Coues and Palmer." This unfortunate episode convinced Palmer that he must keep to himself and share his efforts with no one.

Perhaps his feelings were somewhat soothed when he learned what important plants he had discovered. One was the eight-foot silvery-plumed beargrass, *Nolina parryi*, one of the distinctive plants of the southwestern deserts. It grew in huge clumps on rocky slopes and was used by the Apaches in the weaving of their fine baskets and mats.

His mountaintop century plant also proved to be new and was named *Agave parryi.* This was the first of several century plants he would discover in the Southwest and in Mexico, and he came to appreciate their fleshy sword-leaves and tall flower stalks as the choicest of natural treasures. The century plant provided food, drink, soap, fiber, flour, and sugar for anyone clever enough to put it

Century plant

Palmer penstemon

to use. It was the staff of life in Mexico, where over 170 kinds flourished. Palmer would later write:

> A plant that contains so much fibre, surpassing in length and strength many other fibres in use for cordage and for paper, must some day be cultivated on the desert wastes of the United States. (From *American Naturalist*, December, 1873)

Although his advice went unheeded in the Southwest, some forty other countries today grow century plants for their fiber.

Best of all, the handsome white and lavender wild flower so fragrant on every hillside was named for him: *Penstemon palmeri*, the Palmer penstemon or beard-tongue. It blanketed Arizona slopes in the spring and early summer, and would one day be a favorite wild flower along the nature trails of Zion National Park in Utah.

7

Camp Lincoln

In October 1865 Edward Palmer joined the army again. His services as a doctor were desperately needed on the bloody frontier, and he was sent at once from Fort Whipple to Camp Lincoln, sixty miles away in the Verde Valley.

Till his dying day, Palmer would never forget that trip. The troopers he accompanied traveled by mules and a wagon, reaching the edge of a high rim overlooking the valley just as the sun was setting. Far below them stretched the dusty gray desert with the green Rio Verde snaking its way along one side. The road to the bottom was not only steep and crooked, but so rough they dared not take the wagon down till morning.

Thus the weary troops had to unload the supplies and pack them down the mountain on their backs. The heavi-

Camp Lincoln

est articles were lowered by ropes for a mile and a half. Tired as they were, the men's jumpy nerves kept them on the alert. So many Indian attacks had been staged on this slope that it had come to be called Grief Hill.

Palmer was the last one down. He insisted on carrying his own gear. The others were much too busy making camp to notice how carefully the doctor hid his supplies in the brush some distance away. All that remained on top of the rim was the wagon itself and a desk full of company papers. Everyone sighed with relief that not an Apache had appeared.

Morning brought them little comfort. A detachment sent up to fetch the wagon and desk found them a smoking heap of ashes. Apaches had followed their every move!

As for Palmer, it was not the Indians but another matter that had him worried. Every scientific collector on the frontier was faced with the same problem: how to preserve the alcohol that was needed to preserve the specimens. It was a five-gallon keg of whisky that Palmer had so carefully hidden the night before. If these frontier soldiers found it, there would be little left for pickling the strange new lizards and snakes he spotted at every turn. All at once he knew what he would do.

He dragged his keg over to the breakfast fire. The wide-eyed soldiers followed his every move as the little man uncorked the top and, without a word, poured in two pounds of white powder. Palmer's own notes tell the rest:

> One anxious voice called out "Doctor what's that
> you put in?"
> "Arsenic," I replied.
> Then he said "my free drinks are ended. I had 3
> yesterday."
> The keg could now be left. Science and the specimens
> made it safe. (From Original Unpublished Manuscripts,
> 1865–1889, in Special Collections, University of Arizona
> Library, Tucson)

Camp Lincoln itself was the sorriest-looking army post Palmer had ever seen. Orders required the Arizona troops to build their own shelters from whatever material they could find at the site. Since there were no timber trees near by, the camp was nothing but a clump of pole-and-dirt huts built Indian style. There were three doors made from boxes, but not a piece of real lumber nor a window in the whole camp. Sun and rain alike found their way inside, making the soldiers miserable.

The army could hardly be blamed. It had neither the money nor the supplies to equip every little outpost needed to defend the scattered settlers against Apache raids. During the Civil War the Federal cavalry had pulled out of Arizona altogether. This left miners, ranchers, and friendly Indians at the mercy of the brutal Apaches. They had plundered the country at will. Now the troops were back, but nowhere were they strong enough to end the bloodshed.

Camp Lincoln's troopers were as rough-and-tumble as the camp itself. There were two companies of "tame" Indians, a few white men, and some Mexicans. Each man of the First Arizona Volunteers had enlisted for one purpose: to fight his deadly enemy, the Apache. Such a mixed outfit was often looked down upon by the regular cavalry. But according to Palmer, they did a better job than most all-white units, for they fought the Apaches at their own game.

Every few days a detachment went out on a scout against the Apaches. They traveled at night on foot over rough country, each man carrying a rifle and a 28½-pound pack. The pack held dried beef, *pinole* (a corn-meal and sugar mixture; very refreshing in water, Palmer noted), ground coffee and a cup to make it in, a canteen of water, and a blanket roll. Palmer's pack was heavier than the rest with his scientific material, bottles of alcohol, surgical instruments, and collector's shotgun. By the end of every march the specimens he had stuffed inside more than doubled its weight.

In all, Palmer went on seven scouts against the Apaches. Scout Number 3 was a typical one. With five days' rations on their backs, they set out in the evening, a lieu-tenant, Palmer, and forty-five men. They marched all night and lay up all day. No noise was allowed, nor any fire except for the few twigs each man could burn to boil his coffee. On the second night out, the advanced guards spotted a band of Apaches holed up in hillside caves. The troop attacked at dawn, wiping out the warriors and taking the women and children prisoners. Palmer noted that the squaws were as deadly with the bow and arrow as the braves. He remembered to secure an arrow for the Smithsonian collection.

In spite of the constant danger, Palmer was more than satisfied with Arizona. It was truly a collector's paradise, just as he had guessed. The desert was not the barren wasteland that easterners pictured. It was, in fact, an alto-gether new world, overrun with strange trees like the mesquite, cat's-claw, ironwood, and palo verde, with creosote bushes and rabbit brush, century plants and yuccas, and acres of carpeting wild flowers after the spring rains, not to mention the hundreds of cactuses.

Antelope, deer, and mountain sheep, wild pigs and bobcats, coyotes, foxes, and ringtailed cats, ground squir-rels, jack rabbits, and kangaroo rats lived in the open as he did. Doves and woodpeckers, snakes and lizards, tor-toises and scorpions — all came under his keen collector's eye or into his jars and boxes.

Into his notebook went every detail of his collecting jaunts. The words were calm, serious, and scientific as Palmer was himself. But did he always keep a straight face? Or was he, perhaps, smiling the day he wrote about the troops stuffing themselves with the fruits of the yucca plant?

Yucca plant

On one occasion the troops in Northern Arizona captured a quantity of the dried fruit from the Apaches, and, being sweet, it was generally eaten; and for some time neither salts nor castor-oil were needed from the medicine chest, as this fruit proved to be a vigorous cathartic when dry. (From *Report of the Commissioner of Agriculture for the Year 1870*)

The Verde Valley held another attraction for a man like Palmer. There were many natural caves in cliffs beside the river, and in them an ancient race of people had built their dwellings. Palmer was soon exploring every one of them within reach, squeezing through their tiny doors, no bigger than windows. He found broken pottery, corncobs, and yucca-fiber sandals, all covered with the dust of centuries. Indian relics were always a desirable collector's item, so Palmer carefully packed away any he found.

The Verde settlers speculated that the Aztecs from Mexico had built these cliff dwellings before they migrated south to the Valley of Mexico. It would be years before archaeologists finally determined that the dwellings had been built instead by a local Pueblo people called "Sinagua." The largest cave pueblo Palmer investigated later came to be called "Montezuma Castle," after the famous Aztec leader. Today it is visited by thousands as Montezuma Castle National Monument.

The summer of 1866 started on a sour note. Palmer was thrown from a mule while on his way down Grief Hill, and suffered a bad head wound. What hurt him more was the fact that he could not go along on Scout Number 8. The unit was hiking into a new area, "full of rare specimens," Palmer sighed, that he would never see. The only thing the men brought back was an old Apache prisoner whom they nicknamed "the paymaster." They had not been paid in months and figured this was as close as they would ever come to seeing the real one!

Then the rains began. Strange for rain to pour down on a desert with such fury. Palmer learned that either there was no rain at all for months and even years, or

"Montezuma Castle"

there was too much. He jotted down a note about the summer storms:

> Thunder is not near so loud as in Europe, but the thick bars of lightning remain visible for a much longer time and quiver 2 or 3 times before they dart into the earth, and the chains of fire would twine like serpents around the clouds with marvelous brilliancy. (From Original Unpublished Manuscripts, 1865–1889, in Special Collections, University of Arizona Library)

One bolt struck a nearby cactus and set it to burning so fiercely that Palmer sent a man to put it out before it could spread. The Verde settlers complained they had never known so many afternoon storms.

Worst of all was the "intermittent fever," or malaria. No sooner was Palmer on his feet again after his head injury than he and the entire camp were struck down with fever. Sixty men in a single day! The Verde settlers came to their rescue when only one trooper was left on his feet. A Mr. Ramstein carried Palmer to his cabin. Twice the young doctor thought he would die, but each time he "felt as though I had not done all that was allotted for me and became resolute." They sent him to the hospital at Fort Whipple as soon as possible.

The final blow was not his sickness. It was his hard-won collections left behind in Camp Lincoln. The commanding officer promised to send them on, but somehow never did. Palmer had no chance to visit the camp again for three long years. By then there was nothing left but a scrapbook. The carefully pressed plants, the boxes of bird and animal skins, the pottery from the Indian ruins — all had been thrown out or carried away by the soldiers.

8

Camp Grant

For a man of his day, Edward Palmer was curiously unprejudiced against Indians. In the untamed Southwest, where most white men passionately believed that the only good Indians were dead ones, Palmer was a man apart. The rough ways of this rough land never rubbed off on him. To him Indians were fascinating scientific curiosities at first, to be studied carefully. Later, when he knew them better, he came to regard many of their practices as superior to the white man's, perhaps because they too loved and used wild plants.

He never failed to remark over the wonderfully clever articles they made from plants. "We are astounded in beholding their workmanship," he said, concerning their use of plant fibers in basketry, "they simply took nature's gifts and made the best of them . . . The finest works of modern art are produced in places no more elegant than the Pima's summer shed." (From *American Naturalist*, August, 1885, and April, 1882)

Already he knew the "tame" Indians well. He had soldiered side by side with them during the Civil War and at Camp Lincoln. Now he was about to meet the wildest of the "wild" Indians face to face.

"Apaches," the Spanish first called them, from a Yuma word meaning "warriors." Warriors they were, without equal in the American Southwest and northern Mexico. They were not a single tribe, but several completely separate bands such as the Chiricahuas, the Mescaleros, the Coyoteros, and others.

They had been fighters from the very beginning. They did not herd sheep or grow corn or gather berries for a living. Instead, they carried out daring raids against their Indian and Mexican neighbors for the sole purpose of stealing and killing. They lived by a warrior's code in which the best man was the one who could steal without being caught and kill without being killed. They believed in telling the truth, paying their debts, and loving their children. But they felt no pity for their enemies.

The coming of the American soldiers to Arizona and New Mexico baffled these Apache bands. Here were men who showed no fear of them, who fought just as hard as they did and with superior weapons. Many of the Apaches were soon quite willing to call it a draw and leave the Americans alone — at first.

Then suddenly the American cavalry withdrew from the Southwest to fight in the Civil War. The Apaches

Apache Indian

considered this to be a retreat of defeated forces. They stepped up their raids against defenseless American settlements. But settlers continued to pour into the territory when gold and silver were discovered in the mountains. By the time the troops finally returned after the war, the Apache problem had reached the point of no return. Something drastic had to be done, and quickly.

Most settlers favored wiping out the Apaches completely. But Congress in Washington and the more advanced Eastern states cried out against this idea. Still, the cavalry began with a series of death-dealing raids. But the Apaches melted into the mountains whenever the troops appeared. Foot soldiers like Palmer's companions at Camp Lincoln had more success. Yet it was apparent that American troops would never succeed in completely wiping out these warriors in their own rugged mountain strongholds. A new approach was in order.

Edward Palmer found himself an eyewitness to the government's next attempt at solving the Apache problem. He was assigned to the Camp Grant Military Reservation east of Tucson, Arizona, as soon as his health permitted. He was still a sick man, but not too ill to notice certain changes in the army's policies. If the Apaches would stop their raiding and settle down on government reservations, then the army would feed them and call off its manhunt.

It was to be a period of treaty-making, a brief lull in the bloody Indian campaign when each side would test the other's honesty. Unfortunately, treaties agreed upon by certain bands of Apaches were often broken by others, for the Apaches were never a unified nation. Nor did the white settlers feel bound to keep promises made by the army. The peace was short-lived, but it brought Palmer closer to these wild people than he would ever be again.

He watched in fascination the day the first peace treaty was to be signed. The chiefs of several Apache bands filed into the camp. Their fringed buckskin breechclouts, knee-length moccasins, and cloth headbands were no different from those worn by any Apache brave. But something about their bearing made Palmer aware that these men were truly leaders. They had indeed been chosen by their people for their wisdom, strength, and bravery.

Yet it was evident they were uncomfortable in an enclosed area full of white men. The slightest unusual noise or movement set them on edge. When at last it was time to sign the treaty, the Camp Grant officers excused themselves to don their dress uniforms and swords. These were meant to impress upon the chiefs the importance of the treaty. They were impressed, but in a totally unexpected manner. At the sight of the officers dressed as if for battle, the Apaches fled! Palmer remarked:

> It is not often that people get frightened at uniforms, but this benighted people have been so long and roughly handled by the Mexicans and Americans, now being at war with them, and not seeing uniforms on when they entered camp, when they now entered the room to talk, and seeing the strange glitter, they became alarmed and left. (From Original Unpublished Manuscripts, in Special Collections, University of Arizona Library, Tucson)

Being hunted down like outlaws in both the United States and Mexico finally had its effect on the Apaches.

Many of them were literally starving. It was the promise of free rations once a week that finally lured them back to Camp Grant. Palmer was present at the actual signing of the treaty. Chiefs from the Tontos, Coyoteros, Mescaleros, and Arivaipas gathered in the commander's office. No one knew what to expect. Reported Palmer:

> One of the Aravaypas hereupon stepped forward, opened the face of the clock, held the written part (of the treaty) to the face, clapped his hand to his breast, held up both hands towards the clock in a supplicating attitude, and uttered a prayer that peace might always exist between them. (From Original Unpublished Manuscripts, in Special Collections, University of Arizona Library, Tucson)

Afterwards the Apaches gathered once a week at the camp in great numbers to receive their rations. Palmer made it a point to watch. One ration day in February he saw a brave steal a shoeing knife from the blacksmith shop. The Indian was caught red-handed and made to stand on a barrel in front of the guardhouse with a log of wood on his shoulder. There were angry mutterings from his companions at this treatment. As Palmer edged closer to the excited crowd, a nearby brave suddenly made an attempt to steal his watch. The little doctor shooed him away firmly, but wondered to himself: what kind of people were they, who would try to steal so openly as if it were some kind of game? He was determined to find out.

From time to time family groups would set up camp within the military reservation, constructing their brush wickiups and carrying on their daily tasks. Their cooking fascinated Palmer. He was something of a cook himself — as most frontiersmen had to be — and was always seeking new methods and new foods. He watched the women dig pits, line them with hot stones, and fill them with the cores of century plants. After baking for twenty-four hours, these cores resembled loaves of brown sugar and tasted nearly as sweet. Palmer bargained with the Indians for this *mescal*, as it was called, not only because the troopers loved it but because it helped prevent scurvy, a common dread in early Arizona military posts.

He also admired their cooking baskets woven of willow and waterproofed with pine resin. They would drop sizzling hot stones from the fire directly into the food in the baskets until it was cooked. Palmer claimed that the soot on the stones was harmless and actually flavored the food. When the stones were removed, the Indians licked them clean before tossing them away.

"A glance at the methods of cookery may raise a smile," remarked Palmer, "but the ingenuity exhibited in many cases cannot be denied."

Palmer came to admire the Apaches for traits he was surprised to find among such savage fighters and clever thieves. "It is always customary for one who has anything which others have not, to share as long as it lasts. Their liberality to each other makes them wonder at the selfishness of civilized people." (From *Zoe*, March 1890)

He had always heard that Indians were great gamblers. After observing the Apaches for a full summer, Palmer had this to say about it: "Women are as passionately addicted to gambling as the men, and either sex will lose money, clothing, ornaments or any of their possessions with as little murmuring as any other race of people — gamblers are gamblers whether red, white or black." (From *Zoe*, March 1890)

Most of all, Palmer was fascinated by the medicine

men. As a doctor, he admired their healing arts. As a plant collector, he sought their strange herbs. As the inquisitive person he always was, he wanted to know all their secret beliefs. To find out was not easy. They would not talk about themelves to strangers. As often as not they would make up answers just to stop him from asking. Nor would they tell about their religious beliefs or charms, for then they believed the sun would be angry.

One ration day Palmer succeeded in luring several of the older men into his dispensary by promising them tobacco. He had them sit at his table while he showed them his medicines and asked about theirs. Through sign language and the few Apache words he knew, he was able to understand a good deal. As usual, they were nervous inside the building, and he could see their eyes darting rapidly this way and that. One was just in the middle of explaining how he could cause the rain to fall, when he happened to spot Palmer secretly jotting down notes half concealed under the table. Abruptly they all arose and departed without a word.

The next week Palmer tried again:

> I told them that I did not wish to do anything to
> cause more sickness and death among them they
> frequently afterwards came for more tobacco; but
> never to finish their talk. They had seen me write under
> the table thus they took umbridge at the talking paper.
> (From Original Unpublished Manuscripts, in Special
> Collections, University of Arizona Library, Tucson)

One medicine man called Tseiland wore a hat that Palmer greatly admired. It was made of buckskin in the shape of a half-moon, with turkey and hawk feathers as well as shells and turquoise for decorations. Palmer made every effort to buy it, but the old man would not sell. He said the sun would be angry with him and take away his powers. Then his tribe would become enraged and kill him. He never allowed the hat to leave his head day or night except to wash his hair — which was not often.

Palmer did succeed in securing an Apache medicine bag with buttons and beads and bones all over it. His collection also included a necklace made of seeds, roots, buttons, and beads. Such necklaces were worn by the women not only for beauty but also for protection against disease. Whenever they become sick, they would chew up whatever root was needed for medicine from their necklace. This was Palmer's first important collection of modern Indian arts and crafts, and he sent them of course to the Smithsonian.

Collecting desert birds was another matter. The region around Camp Grant abounded in new birds, nests, and eggs. Palmer could hardly wait to get started. Since most of the species were within sight of camp, it seemed almost too easy. It was. His commanding officer suddenly banned all shooting of weapons on the military reservation. That meant Palmer would have to hike two miles before he was over the boundary and free to hunt. The order added that such shooting could not be distinguished from an Indian attack.

Palmer disagreed. The report of his small shotgun sounded nothing like the rifles used by the Indians. Besides, he had always notified the sergeant of the guard where he was going. He would not have complained so bitterly had his health been better. But a four-mile walk out and back was almost more than he could manage.

When he explained to the officer how much birds from this region were wanted by the Smithsonian, the man replied with a shrug, "I don't like the Smithsonian, am down on it, for it is supported by money that ought to belong to my family as by my mother's side the Smithson's were related." (From Original Unpublished Manuscripts, in Special Collections, University of Arizona Library, Tucson)

Nevertheless, Palmer managed to collect one hundred bird skins during his stay at Camp Grant. One was a new desert thrasher, named in his honor *Toxostoma curvirostre palmeri*, the curve-billed or Palmer's thrasher. Today it is the most common and familiar thrasher in the Phoenix-Tucson area. Picnickers in the region's desert parks know it well as the large gray bird on the ground around the picnic tables.

How Palmer managed to do so much collecting without neglecting his medical duties is hard to understand, but he did. From every post he carried letters praising his faithful performance of duties as well as his remarkable success in using herbs and plant remedies when his medicines ran out, something he had been practicing ever since his Paraguay trip.

By August his medicines at Camp Grant nearly did run out. In five months he used seventy-five ounces of quinine and there were still 127 men down with fever. He himself was finally stricken and lay helpless in his little dispensary hut. This would have ended all attempts at collecting for any man but Palmer. As it happened, he secured some of his best specimens while he was down and out. It seems that his pet cat was just feeding a new

Locoweed, Astragalus palmeri

litter of kittens near his bunk. Every time she came in with a mouse or ground squirrel, he would lean over and catch her, take her prey and skin it, and then return the meat to the kittens. In this strange manner he stumbled upon several new kinds of rodents!

Altogether Palmer collected some 250 plants during his seven-month stay at Camp Grant. Many were new and one, a locoweed, was named for him: *Astragalus palmeri.* Again his poor health forced him to ask for a release. Then he traveled overland to California, where he had heard of a certain mineral-water malaria cure. But his real quest was, as always, for new fields to explore. Perhaps this time Washington could help him. He boarded another Panama boat and set off to find out.

9

Indian Territory

Once again Colonel Jesse H. Leavenworth's presence in Washington settled for Edward Palmer the next direction of his career. Leavenworth had just received his appointment to head the new Kiowa-Comanche Indian Agency in Oklahoma, and offered to take Palmer along as agency doctor. He remembered the young doctor's good work in Colorado during the Civil War. But had he forgotten the trouble that arose when Palmer failed to receive his army appointment?

On his part, Palmer jumped at the chance to return to Indian Territory (now Oklahoma). Now at last he could collect the plants he was forced to pass up during his busy war days. Any memory of his bitter feeling toward the Colonel had long since disappeared. He quickly agreed to meet Leavenworth at the end of the month in Kansas

81

City. Meanwhile. he would stop off in St. Louis, Missouri, for a chat with Dr. Engelmann, handler of many of his plant collections.

His usual contact with Engelmann was through letters. He would write him where he was going, and the Missouri botanist would tell him what types of plants he especially wanted. Later, he not only identified and sorted Palmer's plants but often sold the duplicates for him as well. Palmer kept up a steady stream of letters to great American botanists like Engelmann throughout his life, and visited them in person whenever he found himself near their homes. Thus he knew when he left St. Louis for Indian Territory what special plants the herbariums around the country were looking for.

Colonel Leavenworth had no inkling that Palmer's real purpose in returning to Indian Territory was to collect plants. He knew that Palmer had been a good doctor, but had no idea he was also a plant collector. Leavenworth himself was strictly a military man who allowed no outside activities to interfere with his duties. He had been picked for the job of settling the wild Kiowas and Comanches on their new reservation because of his success in dealing with them during the Civil War. He now had high hopes for showing these wandering buffalo hunters how to be peaceful farmers.

He was doomed to failure from the start. It was one thing for the old chiefs to agree to settle down on reservations. It was another for the wild young braves to give up their ponies and learn to farm. Why should they bend their backs in hard labor when buffalo meat was free for the taking? Why should they give up their roaming hunter's life for the drudgery of a farmer? And why, indeed, should an Indian do anything at all to please the white man?

To most of the Plains tribes, the white man would long remain a mortal enemy. It was he who was crowding them off their prairies. It was he who was invading their hunting grounds with railroad tracks. It was he who was slaughtering their buffalo until in twenty years there would be no great herds left. Now this arrogant paleface thought he could give them orders, as well.

Nevertheless, the Kiowa and Comanche chiefs brought in about five thousand of their followers to give it a try. Colonel Leavenworth had set up a temporary camp along the Washita River about twenty miles below the site of old Fort Cobb while he looked for a permanent spot to settle. In came the Indians, setting up their tepee camps and milling around the agency quarters. Palmer found himself giving medical treatment to about fifty Indians a day from the start.

He also had to protect every movable object from their grabbing hands. These people were not meek reservation Indians, but proud and insolent warriors. Nor were they like the fierce but starving Apaches he had known in Arizona. The braves carried their weapons wherever they went and even the squaws had wicked-looking butcher knives tucked in their belts. There was no talking to them nor bargaining for tribal secrets as he had done in Arizona. They came when they wanted, took what they wanted, and treated the Indian agents as little more than dirt under their feet.

Not that the little doctor feared them. On the contrary, he never gave it a thought that he was one lone white man against five thousand savages. He just would not put up with their rude behavior. It is not clear what started the trouble, but Palmer soon became a bone in the Indians' throats. They went out of their way to annoy him. How he responded is not known, only that he became a special object of their hatred and received many threats.

Colonel Leavenworth did little to help him. Again he was much too busy with problems of his own. Soon after arriving, the entire agency had to be moved to its permanent quarters at the head of Eureka Valley overlooking the river. Then there was trouble with the peaceful Wichita Indians who already occupied the land. And still the Kiowas, most defiant of the Plains tribes, refused to stop their raiding of ranches and settlements all the way to Texas.

But spring was in the air, and Palmer ignored the brewing trouble to spend every spare moment collecting the growing number of plants, animals, birds, and snakes. The Indian squaws did not bother him as he poked about, and even allowed him to watch as they cooked or fished or dug their useful roots and herbs.

One lily he collected came from a lake near old Fort Cobb. The Comanches called it *currates* and boiled it to eat. Palmer thought it tasted much like Irish potatoes. Another root was crushed in a solution and poured into ponds to bring the fish to the top for easy catching. One white prairie flower with a milky juice had an even more clever but illegal use. The braves rubbed it over the brands of cattle they had stolen, so that no trace of a hide mark was left when the animal's hair grew back.

Palmer never grew tired of tracking down the strange native uses of plants. He noted that sumac leaves were smoked by the Comanches, that a certain black trailing plant was powdered and eaten for a pain in the stomach or used for colic in horses, and that one of the freed Negro slaves in the Chickasaw Nation might pick a plant called "love vine," fasten it to another plant, and if it grew, know that his girl friend really loved him.

Altogether he collected 484 specimens during his seven-month stay. It was later declared one of the most valuable plant collections ever to come from Indian Territory. But again his important field notes were scattered and did not accompany the flowers they described. The snakes, frogs, and toads Palmer gathered also impressed the authorities enough to include them in a new and important book on the subject.

But Colonel Leavenworth was hardly impressed. Although Palmer carried out his medical chores, the Colonel objected to the time he spent at natural history pursuits such as "skinning a skunk."

Things came to a head when Leavenworth made a formal complaint about him to the Indian Commissioner. And worse still, a party of Indians raided Palmer's dispensary and were about to destroy his collections when they suddenly came upon the snake skins. After much excited muttering, the whole band left as abruptly as it had come. Snake skins, they knew, were the property of the medicine man, and few Indians would meddle with such a dangerous fellow!

Palmer was miles from civilization, and had nowhere to turn for help until he met Major Shanklin, the agent in charge of the Wichita headquarters down the valley. The Major gave him his complete sympathy. He was already set against Leavenworth and his policy of bringing the wild Plains tribes into an area settled by peaceful groups like the Wichitas. He not only defended Palmer's right to collect, but also wrote to the Indian Commissioner in Palmer's behalf.

Perhaps this was more than Leavenworth could take. At any rate, in May he had Palmer officially removed from his Kiowa-Comanche Agency. Major Shanklin promptly invited the doctor to move to the Wichita Agency, which he did.

But Palmer's problems with the Kiowas were far from finished. Now that he was living with their sworn enemies, the Wichitas, the Kiowas made a secret plan to get rid of the hated white medicine man. No one at the Wichita Agency had any idea of the danger lurking so close at hand. Any rumors they might have heard were probably shrugged off as just more empty threats. Yet Palmer and the Major would have been killed in their sleep but for the loyalty of a single Indian.

He made his stealthy way to Palmer in the morning and warned him of the plot against his life and the plan to destroy the Wichita Agency. Palmer quickly gathered together his belongings and hurried from the Eureka Valley. That night the agency building was burned to the ground.

Who this mystery Indian was, or why he warned Palmer, may never be known. Major Shanklin later referred to him as one of the Kiowas. But Palmer himself seems to have left a clue forty-three years later in his will:

I direct my said executors to procure a picture of
Black Beaver, a Delaware Indian, who once saved my
life, and that of Major Shankland, an Indian Agent,
and have the same pictures suitably framed and hung
up in the Indian Collection of the Smithsonian Institute
in Washington, D.C. and the Expense thereof to be paid
out of my estate. (From Registrar of Wills, U.S. Court
House, Washington, D.C., Administration 18,023)

Once clear of the Eureka Valley, Palmer relaxed and
even managed to collect a few plants on his four-day trip
down to Cherokee Town, the closest civilized settlement.
He spent four more months in Indian Territory gathering
the material to complete his outstanding collection. Then
in September 1868 an attack of "congestive feaver" cut
short his activities and started him back again on his long,
familiar road to Washington.

10

Arizona Trails

Professor Spencer Fullerton Baird unfolded a neatly written letter and glanced through its contents once again. He nodded firmly. There was no doubt about it — Edward Palmer was just the man for the job. He had spent nearly twelve years close to the Indians on the western frontier. He could collect plants and animals and Indian artifacts with equal ability. And now, according to this letter, he was on his way to Washington looking for a position.

Professor Baird had been in charge of making collections for the Smithsonian Institution now for almost twenty years. All this time he had been striving to improve relations between the various branches of science and to erase the bitter rivalry that so often arose. Sending out several rival collectors was senseless, he maintained, when one would do. In Edward Palmer, he knew he had a man who would satisfy all the divisions. Not only was Palmer experienced in all branches of collecting, but also in dealing with Indians. Baird dipped his pen in ink to draft the appointment.

So it was that Dr. Edward Palmer left Washington for Fort Defiance, Arizona, on March 14, 1869, as a general agricultural explorer for the Smithsonian Institution, the United States Department of Agriculture, and the Army Medical Museum, his first full-time job as a collector.

Besides collecting, he was to look for new crops or new locations for familiar crops. But most important of all, he was to gather and record as much of the Southwest's vanishing Indian culture as possible. With more white settlers streaming into the new territories every year, the ancient ways would soon be changed beyond recognition.

At Fort Defiance Palmer joined Reverend Vincent Colyer, the new Indian Commissioner, and the two of them set off at once on a visit to the Hopi Indian villages a hundred miles away. They traveled by ambulance wagon and horseback with a detail of soldiers and four Navajo guides to lead the way.

There was no road, just a rough horse trail winding miles through the arid, barren Navajo reservation lands. But Reverend Colyer could find no fault. Nothing could dampen his persistent high spirits. He saw, instead, how easily the trail could be made a good wagon road. When the ambulance broke down in a quagmire far back on the reservation, he had no complaints, but applauded the Navajos who appeared out of nowhere with ropes and tools to set them on their way.

Colyer loved these people, as he did all Indians. He compared them with the Irish, declaring they were brave, hardy, industrious, restless, and quick-witted, a people ready for mischief, play, or hard work. All they needed was a little guidance. The missionary at Fort Defiance had agreed with him, but at the moment had his hands full with their mischief. Tribal vagabonds had been stealing his chickens, milking his cow, and breaking into his kitchen at night.

Palmer had his own problems with the Navajos. Back at the fort he had been poisoning mice for specimens, but as soon as his back was turned they were stolen by the Indians and cooked!

As usual, he was jotting down every Navajo habit he could wheedle out of the Indians or spot for himself. Prairie dogs were another favorite food, he noted. But the Navajos did not eat bear meat, out of their great respect for the bear. They would not eat eggs of any kind for fear they might hatch in their stomachs. Nor would they eat turkey, because of their belief that bad white men turned into turkeys after they died!

Palmer, with his appreciation of Indians, made an excellent companion for Colyer, who was not welcomed by many white residents of Arizona. They objected to a church man as Indian Commissioner, for they knew he would use brotherly love instead of bullets. But Congress was sick of the harsh treatment of Indians by military men, and hoped a new approach might solve the problem. As it turned out, time alone was the answer. Hostility between white men and Indians would die a natural death, but not for many years.

As Colyer's party continued across the reservation, they ran across the scattered earth-and-timber hogans of the Navajos. Children tended flocks of sheep near by, while women sat beneath trees weaving their colorful rugs and blankets. Commented Palmer:

> The rude Navajo Indian makes a blanket upon one of these hand-looms, which commands not only a good price from white men, but their admiration — yet he is considered a savage — lives in a hut.
> It is not necessary to live in palaces, in order to perform great works, and it is shown by our ancient and modern American Indians, that they were equal to emergencies, until compelled to face Europeans with their civilization. (From *American Naturalist*, April, 1882)

But the travelers' main goal was the seven Hopi pueblos perched high on three rocky mesas deep in the Navajo reservation. They rode twenty-three miles the first day, thirty the second. The third day was Sunday and they rested while Reverend Colyer preached to them. By the end of the sixth day their water was dangerously low, and no well for twenty-five miles — another day's ride. They somehow dragged themselves the endless distance to life-saving Bird Spring on the seventh day, and on the next finally drew to a halt at Oraibi, the principal Hopi pueblo.

Colyer's party had been expected and was welcomed with great rejoicing. Between one and two thousand people turned out of their adobe apartment houses to greet them with cheering as they mounted the rocky mesa cliffs to the village on top.

The exhausted travelers first looked to their horses. They asked the chief of the pueblo if they might have some corn. They were surprised to see him climb to the roof of his dwelling and call aloud in the manner of a town crier. Soon women streamed from adobe houses carrying flat hand-woven baskets full of corn, more than enough. They wanted nothing in return, but Colyer insisted upon giving them some flannel which he had brought for the purpose. Then it was the Indian's turn to be surprised when they saw the white men feed the corn to their horses. It was raised with so much difficulty in their dry land that they used it only for themselves.

The chief then invited them to his three-story house to dine. Proudly he displayed his silver-headed ebony cane, presented to him by President Lincoln when the Hopi chiefs were called to Washington some years back. Next a beautifully woven blanket was spread upon the floor and the guests invited to seat themselves. Food was served from baskets and pottery, but first each diner helped himself to a crisp, paper-thin blue corn cake to be used as his plate and spoon, as well as for food. With it he could dip into the home-grown peaches, the mutton, and the sweet syrup from the roasted hearts of century plants. It was a meal far superior to many he had eaten in white settlements, Palmer declared. Later he was to remember the "blue wrapping-paper bread" and write about it:

> At first it seems dry in the mouth, but it soon softens,
> is quite sweet, and is readily masticated. All three
> of us, doubtless, will remember with pleasure the relish
> which our hunger gave to this singular bread.
> At one house the nicest dried peaches, of their own
> production, well cooked, were set before us, into
> the juice of which the bread was dipped, at the same

time serving as a spoon. (From *Report of the Commissioner of Agriculture for the Year 1870*)

The Hopis still make *piki* today, as their blue corn cakes are called. They taste much like cornflakes.

Before the visitors left, the chief invited them to witness a rabbit hunt that would take place the next morning. Again he mounted to the roof and announced to his people the plans for the following day.

Men, women, and children turned out by the hundreds for the ceremonies preceding the hunt. Then the men formed a huge circle down on the desert, driving the terrified jack rabbits to the center and stunning them with boomerangs thrown at their legs. The women gathered the game to be skinned for blankets and cooked for food. Palmer secured several for his own collection, and a wooden throwing-stick as well. Besides these boomerangs, bows and arrows were the only weapons of the peaceful Hopis. They lived forever in fear of their better-armed enemies, the Apaches and Navajos.

The party followed a different trail back to Fort Defiance which led them through spectacular Canyon de Chelly. In niches along its sheer red sandstone walls clung the remains of ancient cliff dwellings. Along the canyon floor were the flocks and summer brush shelters of the Navajo herders. Colyer was so impressed with the scenery that he stopped again and again to make sketches. Palmer admired the plant life even more, and soon had a fine collection of cactuses. One, a buckhorn cholla, can be seen today growing in the Missouri Botanical Garden.

Back at Fort Defiance, Palmer packed his large collection and had it freighted overland to the nearest railhead. He himself was bound west to Fort Whipple, now Prescott, Arizona, this time with an army escort. On the Fourth of July they reached Arizona's highest mountains, the San Francisco Peaks, and Palmer climbed one to its snow line — always on the lookout for new plants in unusual spots.

He remained at Fort Whipple for a month, making short excursions to nearby points of interest. One took him on a ten-day ride with the cavalry to Bill Williams Mountain. He returned with the type specimen of a new Texas mulberry (now preserved in the United States National Herbarium). And again he journeyed over his old familiar road to Camp Lincoln, now Camp Verde, in search of ancient "Aztec" ruins. One that he explored and collected from was an interesting cliff dwelling in the wall of a great sinkhole, later called "Montezuma Well."

All this was but a preface to the longer trips he was planning that year. After stocking up at Fort Whipple, he took the stage in August across the desert to the Colorado River. His journal traces the route by the wells they stopped at. All travel in Arizona was of necessity limited by the water available. Culling's Well was 250 feet deep, Palmer noted. Its water was free for men, but cost twenty-five cents in gold for each animal. The stage-station operator saw to it that a lantern burned all night on a tall pole above the well frame to guide travelers, so Culling's Well was often called "the desert lighthouse." At Johnson's Well a can of fruit or oysters cost a dollar fifty in gold, according to Palmer's journal.

When they finally arrived at Ehrenberg, central Ari-

"Montezuma Well"

zona's main river port, Palmer boarded the steamer *Cocopah* for a voyage down to the mouth of the Colorado in Mexico. He left the United States just south of Yuma, Arizona, where a desert arm of Mexico cut off the state from the Gulf of California. His visit to Puerto Isabel, Mexico, and the mouth of the river was not successful, for some now unknown reason. So he backtracked up the Colorado to the Gila River and eventually back to Fort Whipple, only to repeat the entire trip in October.

His second visit to the mouth of the Colorado proved much more fruitful. Bird skins, shells, and plants galore filled his bags and boxes. He first met the Cocopa Indians, whose interesting plant products would lure him back to the region again and again. And he even crossed the Gulf of California, fifty miles in a small fishing boat, to the clam flats of mysterious Baja, the strange peninsula of Lower California.

As a preview of the plants he would someday discover there, he brought back a new tall, tubular cactus. Its fruit was dense with long yellow spines used by the Indians for combing their hair. From his description it was named *Cereus pecten-aboriginum*, the Indian-comb cactus.

Onto the San Francisco steamer went his collections, eventually to be shipped to Washington. But over to Tucson, Arizona, went Palmer himself, with many miles of collecting still ahead.

Among his several trips out of Tucson that year was a visit to Camp Bowie at the eastern end of Apache Pass. This was said to be the most dangerous spot on the immigrant road to California because of the many ambushes made by notorious Cochise and his band of Chiricahua Apaches. But Palmer would remember it for its largest native century plant, which he discovered near by. It was later named *Agave palmeri*, the Palmer agave, in his honor by Engelmann. Today it is well known as the largest and one of the most common century plants in the Southwest.

In November he boarded the Mexico stagecoach for a swing down into the border state of Sonora. From Altar to Hermosillo to Guaymas it jolted along, with Palmer

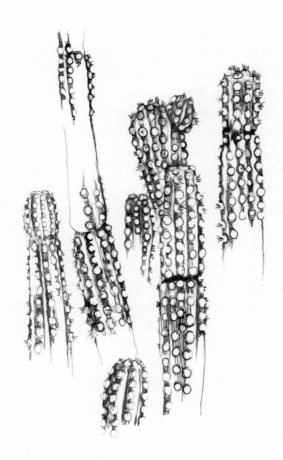

Indian comb cactus,
        Cereus pecten-aboriginum

becoming more and more excited over the growing
wealth of cactuses and tropical plants. The memory
would take him to Mexico many times in the years to
come.

At Guaymas, a charming old Spanish city on a beautiful landlocked bay, he was welcomed by Alexander Willard, the United States Consul, who arranged an even more thrilling trip for him. He was to sail by trading schooner down the Gulf of California to the mouth of the Río Yaqui. Then up the river to a Spanish hacienda, where he would be a guest for two weeks.

Returning from such an out-of-the-way spot might have posed quite a problem for any visitor but Palmer. He merely hired a dugout canoe, then happily chose to walk along the shore most of the way back, collecting as he went, while the puzzled native boatmen poled along beside the strange *gringo*. What kind of *loco* North American would pick leaves and flowers to ride in his canoe, while he himself walked, they wondered.

From Guaymas the most convenient return trip to Washington was by Panama steamer. But first he had to get to an American port. A ship bound for San Francisco solved his problem. When it later anchored off Carmen Island across the Gulf of California, he applied all of his well-known determination to persuade a crew to row him ashore through choppy seas for a final collecting splurge.

His return to Washington from his first full year of collecting was triumphant beyond belief. Professor Baird was more than pleased. The Commissioner of Agriculture was delighted that so many of the plants were new to science and so eagerly sought abroad. Even old Dr. Torrey, the earliest of America's great botanists, wrote him from New York:

I had anticipated much pleasure in spending several days with you at the agriculture department, and in hearing from you an account of your doings and adventures.

You have, in the last few years, done great service to North American botany, and I trust that we shall receive yet greater benefit from your explorations. There are many choice plants to be found in our little-explored states and territories.

I should be delighted to look over your late discoveries, and hope you will be able to spare me duplicates. It is of great importance that the herbarium of Columbia College should be as complete as possible in North American plants. (Reprinted courtesy of *Popular Science Monthly*, c 1911 by The Science Press)

The report Palmer wrote for the agriculture yearbook was his first and most important published work. He drew from his notes and memories the fascinating experiences of thirteen years of plant collecting among the Indians. His twenty-four-page article was entitled "Food Products of the North American Indians." It was so well received both at home and abroad that even a German translation was made. This important study, as well as Palmer's later magazine article on "Plants Used by the Indians of the United States" (*American Naturalist*, October, 1878), is still being used today as a reference for modern books on the subject.

His paragraphs of bare facts were colored by first-hand observation — like his vivid memory of the Indians gorging themselves on mesquite-bean mush:

... all present then collect around the newly-prepared mess, seating themselves on the ground near the dish, and pressing the fingers of the right hand tightly together, at the same time bending the hand so as to form a scoop, dip in without ceremony, and without distinction of rank, age, or sex, forming a grotesque sight rarely to be witnessed outside of an Indian camp. The nearly naked bodies of the Indians soon become smeared from head to foot, and the shaggy appearance of their hair does not exhibit a lively sense of cleanliness. Each face wears a complaisant look, while their tumid abdomens afford certain proof of the quantity consumed.

For once Palmer received the credit due him — and even before his entire collection had arrived. (Several boxes were still on their way by ship from San Francisco.) But February brought the tragic news that the steamer *Golden City*, carrying Palmer's precious boxes, had been wrecked off California.

"When I heard of the disaster every hardship and risk I had endured came to my mind; one by one I recalled some special object of beauty or of interest which I felt I could never replace," mourned Palmer.

Yet things were not as bad as they seemed, for five of his boxes were rescued and turned up in Washington just eight days after he had left on a new expedition to the Southwest.

11

Utah's "Dixieland"

For the first time since Edward Palmer began his travels, a person could cross the entire continent by train. Palmer's ticket took him to Salt Lake City, Utah, on a second trip into the Southwest for the same government departments as before.

Arriving in May 1870, he decided to stop over and hear the forceful Mormon leader, Brigham Young, preach. Afterwards he presented himself and his mission. It was a fortunate move. Young gave him a letter of introduction to the leaders of the Mormon colonists in southern Utah. At a time when the Mormons were being persecuted on all sides, strangers were often viewed with suspicion. But Young's letter was a magic passport assuring Palmer the help and hospitality of every Mormon who read it.

It was snowing the May day he began his long stage

trip south to Utah's "Dixieland," as the Mormon pioneers called their hot desert region where they had been sent to raise cotton. Everything improved the farther south he traveled: the weather, the collecting, and his spirits. Everything except the road. At Ash Creek the ground was covered for miles with axle-breaking volcanic rocks. Dipping into the creek meant sinking into deep sand. Crossing the ancient lava flows meant struggling straight up the wheel-rut "dugways" the Mormons had gouged out, and inching straight down the sheer black ridges.

But the growing things made up for it. Outside Fillmore, Palmer collected a wonderful assortment of cactuses. (One hedgehog prickly pear with especially long spines is growing today in the Missouri Botanical Garden.) On to Beaver he continued by spring buggy. Then through the sagebrush flats to Cedar City and up the red hills to the rim of the Great Basin and the beginning of "Dixie."

St. George on the Virgin River was the principal setlement, and Palmer made it his headquarters. He was not the only one on the lookout for valuable plants. Being far removed from civilization, the settlers themselves were forced to make do with whatever nature provided. They spun and wove their own cloth, dyeing it red with wild-rose pods, yellow with rabbit brush, and black with oak chips and iron. Dandelion roots and prickly pear cactus were home remedies. Cattail down filled cushions and mattresses. Dry bushes made fine brooms. Chewing gum came from milkweed juice, jam from chokecherries, service berries, and wild currants. Even an ice cream

Edward Palmer on pack mule

was made in spring from the inner bark of the cotton-wood trees scraped into a pulpy white mass.

Palmer made many additions to his list of useful plants during his ten days in St. George. He also developed a great respect for the Mormon pioneers. He still had far to go this year, but vowed he would be back.

From St. George the road, such as it was, led across the northwest corner of Arizona and ended at St. Thomas, Nevada. But the only transportation Palmer could find was a threshing machine being hauled over to St. Thomas, another Mormon settlement. The slow plodding of the oxen bothered him not at all, for he could jump off to collect whenever he saw an interesting specimen.

Between black volcanic ridges and red sandstone cliffs they rumbled ever higher into the mountains, camping at the pass on top. Next day they emerged onto a vast, gently sloping desert. It was covered with a forest of tree yuccas called "Joshua trees" by the Mormons because their twisted branches were lifted toward heaven like Joshua's arms. Palmer was fascinated — but thirsty. It had been a dry trip all the way. The remainder of the road to St. Thomas followed the Virgin River, crossing it thirty-eight times! No one would die of thirst here, but the shifting quicksand bottom made every crossing treacherous. Such rough going had Palmer jumping down so often that he soon had a large plant collection.

St. Thomas was the end of the line as far as road travel went. There was, in fact, no traveling at all between there and his destination in Arizona except by muleback.

Palmer bought a mule and saddle, packed himself and his equipment aboard, and set off five days later with the mail carrier as his guide.

It was another trip he would long remember. They left the Virgin River, following a trail to Bitter Springs, which they reached at noon. By afternoon Palmer began to suffer sharp pains and a burning thirst from the bitter mineral water he had swallowed. The trail twisted into deep ravines below the Grand Canyon region of the Colorado River. Hot winds along the canyon floor seemed to come from an oven, forcing the two riders to cover their faces with their broad-brimmed hats in order to breathe at all.

They spent the night at the settlement of Callville along the river, then rose at four A.M. to continue. The trail became so narrow and the dropoffs so steep that the least misstep would have plunged them hundreds of feet below. Even with mules, the trail was so difficult they had to dismount and walk much of the way. Two more days of rough going took them to Hardyville at the head of navigation on the Colorado River, boasting of a population of twenty hardy souls in 1870. Fort Mohave nine miles south was Palmer's destination. He stopped there to collect six boxes of material from the Mohave Indians.

They were an interesting Indian people, much more open with their feelings than many tribes he had met. Smiles, laughter, and affection were not hidden even in the presence of a white man. They were a river people much at home in the water. All but the tiniest were experts at poling their clever reed-bundle rafts back and forth across the river. Babies were pushed across the stream in huge clay pots a yard wide by their swimming parents.

All of them strongly believed in dreams, using the poisonous jimson weed, or sacred datura, to make them more vivid. They would drink a diluted brew from its crushed roots on certain occasions. The powerful drug it contained caused them to experience unusual dreams, which thereafter became an important part of their lives.

As usual Palmer bargained with the men to learn their customs. One old fellow fetched several large spines from a barrel cactus to demonstrate how he made Mohave fishhooks. He soaked the long, flat spines till they were pliable, then bent them into shape and turned them in the fire until they were tempered.

Palmer marveled that the old man could hold the spines directly in the fire with his own hand, even though it was somewhat protected with a wet rag wrapping. The old man finally held up the finished product, explaining in sign language that no barb was needed on such a hook since the river fish would swallow it whole. Palmer had often heard this species of barrel cactus called "fishhook barrel." Now he understood it was not only because of its hooked spines, but for the Indians' clever use.

One of Palmer's published accounts would help popularize the barrel cactus's most famous use:

Travelers in passing through the cactus wastes often resort to this plant to quench their thirst, its interior containing a soft white watery substance, of slightly acid taste, which is rather pleasant when chewed. It is a common sight to see on each side of the road

Barrel cactus, "fishhook barrel"

these plants with a large perforation made by the thirsty traveler. (From *Report of the Commissioner of Agriculture for the Year 1870*)

Palmer went on down to Williams Fork and up that river to the copper mines. Settlements in Arizona were still few and far between, but he knew he could always count on miners for water and shelter. Then too, it still interested him greatly to visit any special attraction an area offered. But his main purpose for venturing inland this time was to secure some fruit from the giant saguaro (sah-WAR-o) cactus. This immense cactus, which raised candelabralike arms up to fifty feet, was perhaps the most remarkable plant in western America. Scientists, museums, and private collectors from the East and even Europe were clamoring for its fruits and seeds. Although it grew only in Arizona (or just over its borders), the saguaro would one day become the best-known symbol of the entire Southwest.

Palmer remembered how the Apaches around Camp Grant had whiled away their days trying to shoot its apple-sized fruit off its giant arm-tips. Nearby desert Indians had often showed up at the camp with gallons of delicious saguaro-fruit syrup for sale at five dollars a jug. Now the season was just right for harvesting the fruits, and Palmer collected a great many.

Returning to the mine settlement, he was suddenly taken deathly ill. His letters do not name his sickness, but no doubt it was malaria again. This was a recurring disease from which he would never be entirely free. The manager of the mine helped pull him through this attack, but it was days before he could ride again.

Saguaro cactus

Months later in Washington the entire experience seemed even more of a nightmare when he discovered that his carefully shipped collection of saguaro fruit was missing. A search finally turned it up in a damp old shed behind the Department of Agriculture greenhouse. Most of the fruits had turned moldy, but a few were rescued and distributed.

Time and again Palmer was plagued with such clumsy handling of his specimens by government officials. Many had little interest in the plants of a dry barren "wasteland." Some of the botanists refused to treat such specimens as valuable. Not only many of his plants but most of his field notes were lost to science in this manner. Kearny and Peebles, authors of the large and important modern book entitled *Arizona Flora*, complain: "It is regrettable that his earlier collections were so carelessly labeled in Washington that doubt exists in many instances as to whether the plant in question actually was found in Arizona."

Palmer returned to St. George, Utah, as he had promised, but not for five years. It was then that he struck up his acquaintance with the Joseph E. Johnson family. The daughter, Mrs. Rosemary Johnson Fox Johnson, now of Salt Lake City, is one of the few living persons who knew Palmer.

She was a girl of ten when Palmer first came to town. She remembers him as a handsome quiet man, always polite and interesting at the dinner table. Her father loaned him his little adobe library building for his quarters. He soon had the fireplace mantel lined with jars and bottles full of snakes. Next to them sat a silver-combed music box which he borrowed from the family and enjoyed listening to as he worked.

Joseph Johnson was a horticulturist whose flower garden was said to be the most beautiful one south of Salt Lake City. Besides flowers, he experimented with fig trees, sugar maples, and pomegranates, and once had over one hundred kinds of grapes on his property. Palmer saw to it that Rosemary and her brothers carried bottles whenever they went into the garden, so they could collect any interesting insects they might run across. He also made each of them flower-press folders for gathering plants whenever they went out into the hills and canyons.

He taught the children how to catch and mount butterflies without spoiling their wings. Several times he hired Rosemary to pull cactus spines out of his hands for twenty-five cents a half hour, after he had come in from a day of collecting. And once when her father was hungry for apple pie, Palmer showed her how to make a delicious one.

But his serious scientific attitude got him into trouble again with the nearby Paiute Indians. When they heard he was collecting Indian handicrafts, they began bringing bits and pieces of things for which he had no earthly use. One old Paiute called "Limpy" brought him an old rope of braided rushes. When Palmer shooed him away, the old man drew his knife, slashed the rope to bits, and threw them at Palmer's feet in a rage.

The doctor's main interest this time was in ancient Indian crafts. He had been hired by the Peabody Museum of Harvard College to excavate Utah's Indian mounds. Not only was his work the very first scientific investigation of pueblo ruins in the Southwest, but it also cleared up a mystery. Stories of some remarkable mound tablets bearing signs of the zodiac had been published in the East. Did this mean the mounds had been built by an Oriental race, perhaps the Chinese? Most local people felt that the Indians they knew were much too backward and primitive to be capable of building anything more complicated than a brush wickiup. But Palmer's work proved the plates to be forgeries and Utah's mounds to be the work of Pueblo tribes similar to the Hopis and Zunis of Arizona and New Mexico.

Nobody knew exactly what the mounds contained or why they had been built. Most of the settlers looked upon them as just more of the countless Indian ruins that had always been there. They were too busy with their own endless struggle to make a living in a hostile land to be curious about old mounds.

Palmer's careful digging showed that most of the mounds were the remains of ancient adobe-hut Indian villages. In some cases new houses had been built over old ones. Others were built wall-to-wall, and some even seemed to be partly underground.

It would be many years before all the pieces of this ancient puzzle would fall into place, before later archaeologists could trace the history of the Basketmaker and Pueblo peoples through their development of cave shelters, pit houses, surface homes, and finally great pueblo apartment houses. But Palmer had made a beginning.

The mound at nearby Santa Clara was roughly circular, about ten feet high, and covered half an acre. In the diggings he found several well-made clay pots, stone drills and hammers, bone and turquoise ornaments, yucca-fiber cloth, a black obsidian knife, flint arrow- and spearheads, and many human bones. Over in Johnson Canyon near Kanab, he discovered cave cliff-dwellings with pieces of pottery, sandals, and corn scattered about on the sandy floor. He poked and pried into every ruin he could find, and in many cases was the only investigator to explore them before they disappeared under the waves of floods and farmers yet to come.

Rosemary's oldest brother joined several other boys helping him dig — with Palmer watching like a hawk to see that none of the ancient relics found their way into a boy's pocket for a souvenir. Instead, the collection went onto a long table in the library. Over 150 pieces were sorted, labeled, and packed for delivery to the railroad depot at Salt Lake City. Altogether nine boxes and four bales of Indian relics were shipped to Harvard, while Edward Palmer made his plans for new discoveries elsewhere.

12

Florida Wilderness

In 1871, for the first time since his western adventures began, Palmer found himself in Washington with no new field to explore. He had been counting on a promised appointment as Indian Agent for the Pima and Maricopa tribes of Arizona, but somehow it fell through at the last moment. This left Palmer packed and ready, with no place to go.

It was Professor Baird who again came to his rescue. He sent Palmer to work for the Commission of Fish and Fisheries along the New England coast. Palmer collected, cleaned, and prepared ocean animals for two long summers, and then returned to Washington for the even longer idle winters. At the end of the third summer, he jumped at the chance to work under the famous Professor Louis Agassiz at the Harvard Museum of Comparative Zoology. But his job petered out with Agassiz's untimely death in December, and again Palmer was stranded.

This time his old botanist friend Professor Gray of Harvard suggested an entirely new direction for his collecting activities. An expedition to the little-known region of Lake Okeechobee in Florida was about to be organized by *Forest & Stream* magazine. If Palmer wanted to go along, he had just two weeks to raise enough money to pay his expenses to Florida. He hurried out to collect whatever he could that might be sold for this purpose.

So it was that Edward Palmer and "a party of gentlemen" left Boston by boat in January 1874, bound for Jacksonville, Florida. The Florida he found was far different from the tourist resort it would some day be. It was a dense subtropical wilderness, with its few small settlements mainly along the coast. There were orange plantations, lumber centers, cattle ranches, and sponge fisheries. But poor transportation isolated much of the interior. Water travel along the rivers and lakes was the only dependable means of movement into inland Florida.

The Jacksonville that Palmer found was a bustling lumber and turpentine town, Florida's second largest city, with a population of 17,000. Key West was first with only a thousand more. Miami was yet unborn, still a wild, barren coastal strip. Lake Okeechobee itself was a mysterious and elusive body of water somewhere in the heart of the Florida wilderness. Frederick A. Ober, leader of the expedition, had attempted to reach the lake two years earlier, but failed. So it remained lost and romantic. Who knew what ancient ruins or strange plants and animals it might conceal?

The expedition boarded the St. Johns River steamer in February, traveling 275 miles down to the portage opposite Sand Point, now Titusville. Here they carried their equipment the six miles over to the Indian River and continued on down to Fort Pierce. Turning inland, they loaded their boat and supplies aboard an ox wagon and set out for Fort Basinger on the Kissimmee River.

Ober later wrote letters to *Forest & Stream* describing their trip. On the inland leg of their journey, he told how they walked sixty miles, swam two creeks, and waded over twenty miles, with their wagon breaking down twice. The one settler they met informed them that only three white men had been to the lake in the past thirty-two years since the end of the Seminole Wars. He advised them to carry plenty of provisions, as there was said to be no game around the lake.

Their run down the Kissimmee River to the lake was almost too easy. In only two days the swift stream carried them to the lake. But what a disappointment! The shore was an impenetrable swamp with not a solid spot of ground on which to camp. The lake itself was nothing but an immense puddle, a shallow inland sea on which a boatman could easily row himself out of sight of shore, yet touch bottom with an oar. There was nothing new to see, no ancient ruins, no plants or animals any different from those in other parts of Florida.

To make matters worse, they would have to hike all the way back to Fort Basinger on foot. The swift current of the Kissimmee, which had swept them down to the lake, now blocked all attempts at upstream travel.

Being short on provisions, the party started back at once. Palmer would ordinarily have cheered such an opportunity for plant collecting. But for once the weather and marshy terrain were too much for him. Day after day the sun glared down on the swampy flatlands with a steamy, humid heat. Everything turned hot, wet, and soggy — their clothing, the ground they walked upon, even their brains, it seemed.

Palmer thought he saw hills ahead, an almost unknown feature in that part of Florida. But the gray-green humps turned out to be rounded clumps of trees, not earth. They were cypress hammocks rising out of marshy prairies and dripping with gray beards of Spanish moss.

As if the heat and water were not enough, the men were attacked by hordes of vicious mosquitoes. Palmer's clothing was actually bloodstained from their bites. Collecting of any kind was all but forgotten. Their only thought was of pushing on to the fort.

In this mood Palmer passed up many likely-looking plants before one at last caught his eye. It was a yellow water lily that somehow reminded him of something important. But what? In his exhausted, dazed condition he could not put his finger on it. Had he seen one like it in Paraguay? No. In some botanical garden? No. Still, he forced himself to collect several specimens and pack them away carefully.

After eight endless days the party finally reached the fort. Most of the travelers were anxious to leave all of Florida behind them as soon as possible, but Palmer hesitated. Although they had found Lake Okeechobee, the expedition could hardly be considered much of a success otherwise. The only way Palmer could salvage his investment seemed to be by staying on in Florida to collect more plants — which he did.

After the others left, he continued collecting along the Indian River till the end of March. Then back up to Jacksonville and across the peninsula to Cedar Keys. From there he took the passenger steamer down to Key West.

The palm-fringed islets, the clear warm waters, and the abundance of coral-reef life kept him occupied until July. Then over to the Bahama Islands he went for three more weeks to collect an outstanding series of algae and sponges.

Upon returning to Key West, Palmer began working his way north along the chain of keys to the mainland, collecting as he went. He stopped for a while at a small settlement on Biscayne Bay, near the future site of Miami. The most interesting plant he found in the area was the "comptie" or coontie, a trunkless fern-palm of the genus *Zamia*. The Seminole Indians of the region used its underground stems for making a starchy flour, the most important item in their diet. Palmer was happy to see the white settlers also setting up several mills to manufacture it. He was always promoting such plant uses. After cooking with coontie flour, he reported:

> The white starch is very nutrious and makes excellent puddings, much nicer than sea moss, farina or corn starch; in fact, it is equal to any starch for domestic or manufacturing purposes. (From *American Naturalist*, September, 1875)

He would be pleased to know that this plant still supplies a commercial product known as "Florida arrowroot" today.

Unlike most plant collectors of his day, Palmer did not limit his observations of new plants to their descriptions alone, but also included interesting details about any animals or insects associated with them. Around every coontie plant Palmer found the beautiful orange butterfly *Eumaeus atala*, called "comptie moth" by the settlers. He caught several for museums in the North. "They fly low, with a slow, measured motion, alighting rather suddenly upon the leaves, are taken easily, as they are not shy nor easily disturbed," he noted.

Another American naturalist had also included many associated details in his descriptions. John James Audubon, early painter of the birds of America, always drew his birds against their natural background of special trees or flowers. Suddenly it dawned on Palmer that there was where he had seen the strange yellow water lily from Okeechobee — in one of Audubon's paintings in *The Birds of America*. He remembered now that it was one of the artist's so-called "mystery plants." Plate number 411, the Whistling Swan, showed a yellow water lily completely unknown to science. Botanists had long wondered whether Audubon had made a mistake — or perhaps even made it up.

It was Palmer's lily, the *Nymphaea flava*, that cleared up this long-standing mystery. Upon examining Palmer's specimens, plant scientists found that the great bird artist had indeed made a mistake. Audubon's painting showed the actual blossom of the *Nymphaea*, but the leaves were of a different species altogether.

Palmer's entire Florida collection was a decided success in botanical circles. Professor Gray helped him sell his plants at eight dollars per one hundred specimens. Altogether more than three thousand were distributed, one of his largest collections thus far.

Ten years later his experiences in Florida would again bring him fame. In 1884 he was sent by the Smithsonian to gather "the varied animal resources of the coral reef and sponge regions of Southern and Western Florida" to be displayed at the New Orleans Cotton Centennial Exposition. His collection this time included finely prepared commercial sponges, ornamental corals, and shells — filling *sixty-five* large shipping cases.

But long before his first Florida venture ended, Palmer was pondering his next move. While at Harvard with Professor Agassiz he had read about an attempt to raise a new breed of goats on Guadalupe Island off the Pacific coast of Baja California. This project caught his interest, not for the goats, but for the unknown island plants which would vanish forever once the goats were turned loose. Here was a spot not only remote but never before visited by a botanist. He could not shake the idea from his mind. Even before he left Florida his imagination was carrying him across the continent to San Diego, California, where he could catch a boat to Guadalupe.

13

Guadalupe Island

Palmer knew he would have to hurry if he hoped to collect Guadalupe's plants before the goats did. Arriving in San Diego, he learned the discouraging news that there was no regular boat service to the island. He had counted on one of the coastal steamers plying between California and the west coast of Mexico, but not one included Guadalupe Island on its stops.

The island lay 280 miles southwest of San Diego and about 150 miles off Baja California, Mexico's western peninsula. It had been completely uninhabited up to a year ago when the Guadalupe Island Company had begun its goat experiment. The company hoped to develop a new breed of goats, and the large rugged island offered a perfect, escape-proof pasture for the animals. Several Mexican herders and their families had accompanied the goats to the island the year before.

Red-shafted flicker

Red-eyed towhee

Oregon junco

Palmer finally turned to the company and was able to arrange passage on a company supply schooner in January 1875 for himself and a hired assistant.

His hopes were high the day they set sail. Guadalupe was just the sort of place he was looking for, a remote, long-uninhabited island. All naturalists dream of finding such a spot, for plants and animals often develop strange and different forms when kept isolated on a tiny island. The coming of man usually changes things radically, and Palmer only hoped he was not too late.

As they approached the island, Palmer could see that it greatly resembled the coast of California — low-lying beaches backed by rugged hills, rising to four thousand feet in the north. The island was a spearhead in shape, but its considerable length of twenty-three miles made it impossible to see from one end to the other.

Palmer was delighted at the vegetation he could make out. The lowlands seemed thickly cloaked with shrubs of a greenish-white appearance. The hills were darker green — with some sort of pine trees, he imagined. It would take years for the goats to denude so large and well-wooded an island.

Suddenly a fluttering filled the air around the schooner, and dozens of sparrowlike birds alighted on the ship. At once they began poking behind boxes and under canvas in search of something to eat. They were so tame that one stood looking at Palmer while he proceeded to pop his butterfly net over it. It was some kind of Oregon junco, he decided. Gray head, cinnamon-brown back ... but strangely like juncos he had seen in the Rocky Mountains, rather than like those from the Pacific coast.

Palmer could hardly contain himself. It might be a new species — and so tame! He was reminded of Charles Darwin's renowned voyage to the Galapagos Islands forty years before, of the strange island birds so tame they had to be pushed away before they would fly, of *The Origin of Species* Darwin later wrote based on his Galapagos experiences, stunning the entire world with his theory of evolution. Would Guadalupe be another Galapagos?

The schooner soon landed the eager collector and his helper, along with supplies for the goat herders. A few rude houses constructed by the herders lined the bay where they anchored. Once ashore, Palmer set his assistant to work building a shelter for the two of them. A simple dwelling was all they needed for their temporary stay, and the helper scraped out a snug earthen dugout roofed over with poles and dirt. It would keep out the wind and might even retain some of the sun's warmth. The weather was similar to California's, mostly fair, but with chilling sea breezes, cool nights, and foggy mornings.

As soon as the fog lifted the following morning, they bade farewell to the schooner. Guadalupe would be their home for the next six weeks, till the ship's return in the middle of March.

Palmer started his scientific activities by making a brief survey of the island. Goats were everywhere and had a good head start on the plant collecting, he was sorry to see. Although bushes dotted the lowlands, most of the lesser growth had been stripped away. The midsection of the island seemed the most promising place to begin. It was steep and rugged with many sheer cliffs and deep canyons. Although the goats were there too, so far they had not touched the plants growing in hard-to-reach places.

Palmer soon discovered why. Plants on many of the vertical cliff faces were virtually impossible to reach by goats or men. Nevertheless, he was determined to have them. He solved the problem by devising a noose at the end of a long pole, causing the Mexican herders no end of laughter over the *gringo* who was trying to "lassoo plants."

Palmer ignored their remarks, as he did all distractions while he went about collecting. His only comment was: "Goats were my only rivals, but they made a clean sweep of everything within reach, not discriminating between what was common and what was rare."

He used ropes to scale cliffs and descend into crevices wherever possible. The common red-berried buckthorn was one of the plants he retrieved in this manner. There were only six buckthorn bushes left on the island, he noted. Another plant from this area was a new species of lupine. It later turned out that twenty-one of Palmer's 140 Guadalupe plants were new to science.

One was a wild tobacco whose leaves stuck to the goats' hair, doing much damage. Palmer was glad to collect it before the herders could destroy the few remaining plants. One impressive wild morning-glory hung down for six feet from a crevice in the high rocks. He counted more than a thousand flowers on a single plant.

Three shrubs were among the most common plants on the island: a groundsel called "white sage," a saltbush, and the greenish-white *Franseria* he had noted from the schooner. Groves of California junipers covered much of the island's mid-section. Bent and twisted by the constant wind, they reached no more than fifteen feet in height.

Most impressive trees of all were the Guadalupe cypresses. They averaged forty feet high and seven feet around. Many had already been stripped of their lower bark by the goats, he was sad to see. Palmer counted 236 annual growth rings on one dead stump. At the head of Landrum's Canyon he stumbled onto the oldest of all Guadalupe cypresses: a tree twenty-five feet in circumference which divided into seven huge trunks whose main limbs themselves measured thirteen feet around.

Many of the island's deep ravines and canyons were surprisingly warm. Their steep walls trapped heat from the intense midday sun and successfully kept out the wind, making ideal growing conditions for subtropical trees. One that Palmer found represented an entirely new genus, *Hesperelaea,* and was later named for him *Hesperelaea palmeri.*

But his most important discovery in the eyes of modern tree lovers was the Guadalupe palm. He called it "the only thing on the island with a tropical look." How he admired these trim little fan palms lining the floors of the warm ravines! He would be happy to know that his discovery is just as much admired today as an ornamental palm in many gardens and streets of southern California and southern Arizona.

Its dangling four-foot fruit clusters weighing up to fifty pounds apiece drew goats, birds, mice, and men to sample its sweet marble-sized fruits. Botanists later named the palm *Erythea edulis: Erythea* meaning "Daughter of

Guadalupe palm, Erythea edulis

the West," after Erythea in Greek mythology who dwelt on an island on the western edge of the world; and *edulis* meaning "edible." Although most of Palmer's new plant discoveries were important mainly in the eyes of botanists, the Guadalupe palm would always remain his most appreciated contribution to the residents of the Southwest.

Yet with all of his exciting botanical discoveries, it was Guadalupe's birds that brought him the greatest fame. Every land bird he collected turned out to be a new form. This in itself was a remarkable feat in 1875. Few men of his day who had spent their entire lives collecting only birds had added so many new species and subspecies to the list of known birds. Furthermore, Palmer uncovered a strange relationship. Just as he had guessed when he examined the Oregon junco, it turned out that Guadalupe's birds resembled inland forms and not their Pacific Coast counterparts.

The red-eyed towhee, for instance, was dull gray-brown like inland species instead of coal black like the towhees of California. Palmer watched it scratching among the brush and fallen logs with its peculiar motion of jumping forward and striking back with both feet. Towhees were not common during Palmer's visit and are probably extinct on Guadalupe today.

Another rare bird was the red-shafted flicker, then found only in the pine woods at the north end, and now extinct on the island. Bewick's wren was also scarce and probably did not survive into modern times on Guadalupe. Palmer watched it eating small black insects from the blossoms of the white sage. He collected some of these insects also.

As he turned over stones and logs for other insects, he had to be quick or his insect-loving followers would beat him to the specimens. They were the tame Oregon juncos, nearly hopping into his hand in their haste to devour the bugs he uncovered!

House finches were the principal songsters of the island, easily equaling canaries, declared Plamer. They lived in the warm canyons during the winter, but in summer flocked around and into the herders' houses, making a nuisance of themselves.

Rock wrens lived in the sheltered canyons but often visited the slaughter yards where goats were killed for meat, to glean insects from the drying bones. Ruby-crowned kinglets remained in the warm canyons all year round. Palmer watched the males displaying their red crown-spot while singing, but quickly concealing it when their notes were finished.

Most notable of all Guadalupe's birds was the terrible *calalic*, the Guadalupe caracara. Not only was it eagle-sized, but also the most numerous. Strangely enough, this great hawk-vulture looked more like the caracaras of South America than like any form in Mexico or Central America. Yet it was a distinct species, found nowhere in the world but on Guadalupe Island. Like all caracaras it was brilliantly colored in brown, white, black, and orange, and terrifying in appearance with its hooked beak, great talons, and aggressive attacks on birds and animal victims.

Flocks of caracaras ravaged the goat herds. No kid was safe from their attacks. Mature goats had more success in defending themselves, although they were doomed if several birds ganged up on one. Herders kept up a constant war against the big birds, shooting and poisoning hundreds, but with no apparent effect. Over the

years, however, their efforts have been only too successful, for today the great Guadalupe caracara is gone from
the face of the earth.

Yet the results of Palmer's important Guadalupe work
nearly failed to reach the scientific world. First of all,
Palmer fell seriously ill for several weeks. Inside the damp
dugout he lay for days at a time. Then March passed by
and soon April as well, with no sign of the company
boat. With their food long gone, Palmer and his helper
were forced to live on goat meat and island greens.

By mid-May the situation was desperate. What had
happened to the supply schooner, no one knew. But
Palmer's friends in San Diego at last became alarmed at
his failure to return. They hired a private boat to rescue
the two collectors. By the end of May a weak but happy
Edward Palmer was back in San Diego with his Guadalupe collection, the most important one of his entire
career.

Even for a person spending a lifetime in the field under the most harsh conditions, Palmer seems to have had
more than his share of sickness and accidents. Yet no
physical ills would ever make this determined man give
up his early vow "to spend my life in the prosecution
of science."

While recuperating in San Diego, he continued collecting, this time sea creatures from San Diego Bay. As
he was wading along in shallow water he suddenly felt
an excruciating pain shoot through his left foot. He had
accidentally stepped on a buried sting ray which whipped
its tail barb into his foot. Only the quick action of a
nearby Mexican woman saved him weeks of pain. She

hurriedly boiled up several gallons of a strong solution from a spurge plant called *golondrina*. Palmer plunged his leg into the hot mixture and in a few hours felt relief. He would never forget these simple folk remedies and plant medicines so valuable to the western settlers.

San Diego seemed to be an excellent base for explorations down into Baja California as well as the surrounding mountains, so Palmer stayed on. He was now collecting not only for his botanist friends but also for the coming Centennial Exposition at Philadelphia.

One of his excursions took him to the Cuyamaca Mountains of southern California for a month. There he visited and collected among the Diegueños Indians near Warner's Ranch. He watched the women tattoo their chins with cactus thorns dipped in charcoal. He sampled their baked century plant. He traded for such items as their twine sacks made of milkweed stems. He noted that the fiber gleaned from shredded yucca leaves was a most important plant product, used in making ropes, twine, nets, hats, hairbrushes, shoes, and mattresses. He purchased one of their excellent horse blankets woven from yucca yarn on a native loom. Later he would write of this experience in the *American Naturalist* magazine. Much later, the same Palmer article would prove a most valuable reference for modern writers of plant books and Indian lore.

But for the present, the coming Philadelphia Exposition would be rich in California Indian crafts, for he returned with "two wagon loads of curious things," according to the *San Diego Evening World*.

14

Baja California

Many a botanist had his eye on the mysterious Mexican peninsula of Baja California in the late 1800s. Rumors of its strange plant life had filtered north to California. But the lack of roads and scarcity of water along its rugged mountains and burning deserts made land travel next to impossible. Still, some travelers had dipped into its forbidding wilderness in their search for an easy route into California. From such people Palmer began hearing tales of a great canyon almost impossible to cross, deep in the Cantillas Mountains just across the California-Mexico border.

With visions of the Guadalupe Island canyons still in his mind, Palmer inquired further. He found that if any man could take him there, it would be George W. Dunn, a well-known California insect collector and Baja explorer. He arranged to meet Dunn and two Indian carriers at Campo along the stage route from San Diego to Fort Yuma.

From there they traveled by wagon across the border and into the wild Baja countryside. Through a forest of oaks, pines, and junipers they proceeded into the mountains. The eastern slopes were dry, and soon scattered groves of piñon gave way to cactus and desert shrubs. Suddenly they found themselves on the brink of a tremendous gorge over five thousand feet deep.

Dunn had collected here before, but even he had no easy solution for their descent to the bottom. Climbing a mile down over sheer cliffs and loose rocks was no simple matter. Palmer tried to collect as they went, which led them into several blind alleys. For a while it looked as though they could go no further, neither down nor back up. But eventually the trees on the canyon floor took on size, and soon they were looking up at them instead of down.

Blue palms, thousands of them, lined the dry washes along the canyon bottom, majestic trees up to sixty feet tall with their blue-green fan leaves and graceful pendants of black fruit. Palm canyons like this never failed to thrill Palmer. They were the true oases of the Southwest, tucked away in remote mountain crevices and always a sign of water. In the midst of an utterly desolate desert region a traveler might suddenly come upon one in the mountains of southern Arizona or California or Baja. The contrast of a tropical tree against a barren mountainside seemed to bring out hidden beauty in both.

A trail along the floor proved that man was no stranger here. Being the first canyon south of the Mexican border containing water, it had long been used by travelers, first Indians and later white men journeying from Tijuana or Ensenada in Baja over to Arizona by way of the lower Colorado River. But Palmer and Dunn were the first scientific collectors to visit the canyon.

Palmer gathered between sixty and seventy-five kinds of plants. The most beautiful one was the *chile de la agua*, as the Indians called it. He had never seen a flower quite like it. It grew in clusters around a single spring at the foot of the trail. To keep his hands free for the climb back out, Palmer carried the plants in his hat, tying it to his head for safety. The five-thousand-foot climb up was so much worse than the descent that Palmer thought he would never make it. But he did — to the everlasting gratitude of the scientific world.

When Professor Gray at Harvard received Palmer's collection, he was beside himself. Not only were most of the plants completely new species, but the *chile* was the first representative of an entirely new genus. Gray named the genus *Palmerella* in Palmer's honor (calling the plant *Palmerella debilis*) because, he said, of Palmer's "indefatigable and fruitful explorations of botany of the southwestern frontiers of the United States, from Arizona to the islands off Lower California, in which region he has accomplished more than all his predecessors." (Reprinted courtesy of *Popular Science Monthly*, © 1911 by The Science Press)

But Palmer was not to hold this honor without considerable trouble. Something had gone wrong in his relations with Dunn. It is not clear what had happened or who was at fault. No sooner had Dunn heard about Gray's name for the new genus than he put in a claim, declaring himself to be the discoverer. So insistent was he that another botanist finally renamed the genus *Lobelia* and the type plant *Lobelia dunnii*.

Now it was Palmer's turn to protest. He called on Dunn in person. Dunn told him that he had indeed collected the plant first and given it to the California Academy of Sciences. Palmer then journeyed to San Francisco to check out this claim. At the Academy he found Dunn's specimen, but it was labeled 1878, three years after Palmer had discovered his specimen. Several years had passed since their journey to the canyon, but Palmer could not ever recall having seen Dunn collect the plant on that trip. Palmer finally published his own version of the discovery in *West American Scientist* magazine in 1890, concluding: "if it can be proven that anyone collected it earlier, in the interest of truth I will be glad to have the fact made known." Palmer's claim was finally recognized.

Cantillas Canyon no longer appears on maps. In fact, no one is sure of its exact location today. Palmer described it as being ten miles from Tres Pozos and nearly parallel with Larkens Station, but routes have changed with the years and these locations are also gone. Modern botanists have tried unsuccessfully to locate it, and can only conclude that it is one of the deeper gorges cut into the eastern slope of the Sierra de Juárez range. But because of Edward Palmer's collection, Cantillas Canyon will always remain one of the most important botanical locations in all of Baja California.

Like many a visitor to Baja, Palmer found that inland travel for any distance at all was barely possible. Except along the coasts, most of the peninsula was completely uninhabited and without water. But boat travel to the various settlements on bays along the east coast was more regular then than it is today.

He visited every settlement possible to reach, and then hired local boatmen to transport him out into the Gulf of California to the nearest coastal islands. Some were high volcanic islands white with nesting birds. Others were low, rocky, and barren. But all held out the attraction of being wild, uninhabited spots never before explored by a scientist.

Although within sight of the mainland, most of Baja's eastern islands were effectively isolated by swirling tidal currents, treacherous even in good weather. Huge whirlpools formed around tiny Isla Raza, a mile-square islet outside Angeles Bay. Neither these nor a tidal drop of thirty feet prevented Palmer from landing there and finding the nesting site of thousands of Heerman's gulls.

Farther out in the middle of the Gulf lay San Pedro Mártir, an even more fascinating island. Palmer found its four square miles to be completely covered with a thick cactus forest of giant cardons, or *cardones*, as Mexicans called all tubular tree cactuses.

This particular cardon had been discovered in Mexico three years before, and named *Pachycereus pringlei*, but none had been seen since then. They resembled Arizona's giant saguaros, except that they branched close to the ground with as many as a dozen thick arms rising straight up for twenty feet.

137 | 🌲

Not another tree grew on the island. Indians and Mexicans who visited the place to gather bird guano used the wooden cactus ribs from dead plants as fuel. They also made canes from the straight tough ribs to help them climb the rocky, thousand-foot rise in search of the guano. The remarkable cardon forest supplied these workers with excellent food as well, in the form of its juicy fruits and its seeds. These latter they ground into flour which they mixed with water and cooked between corn husks like tamales. Palmer declared they were "not inferior to pies of more civilized people." All in all, he was able to collect eighteen flowering plants on San Pedro Mártir, one of which was a new composite genus.

Then in May 1876 Palmer journeyed out of Baja and north by stage to San Bernardino, California, for a visit with Dr. Charles C. Parry, a botanist he had known for several years. Parry had invited Palmer to join the plant-collecting party he was forming to ascend southern California's highest peak, San Gorgonio Mountain (locally called "Grayback"). Palmer seems to have had as little luck with beasts of burden as he did with his fellow botanists. On the second day out he was thrown from his horse and injured his spine. His companions made him as comfortable as possible while they returned for a carriage to take him back to town.

An account of the incident was published in the San Bernardino paper saying that Palmer had been left "on the mountain without *grass or water*, with a man to look after him." Although Palmer was disappointed to be laid up, he took it with good humor. As he later remarked: "Everywhere I went for some time afterward, I was pointed out as the man who had been left on Grayback Mountain without grass or water; sometimes I was jocosely addressed: 'Hello, old grass-and-water, how's your back?' " (Reprinted courtesy of *Popular Science Monthly*, © 1911 by The Science Press)

The trip was not a total failure, for Palmer and Parry were able to complete their plans for a wonderful collecting expedition they would soon make together into Old Mexico.

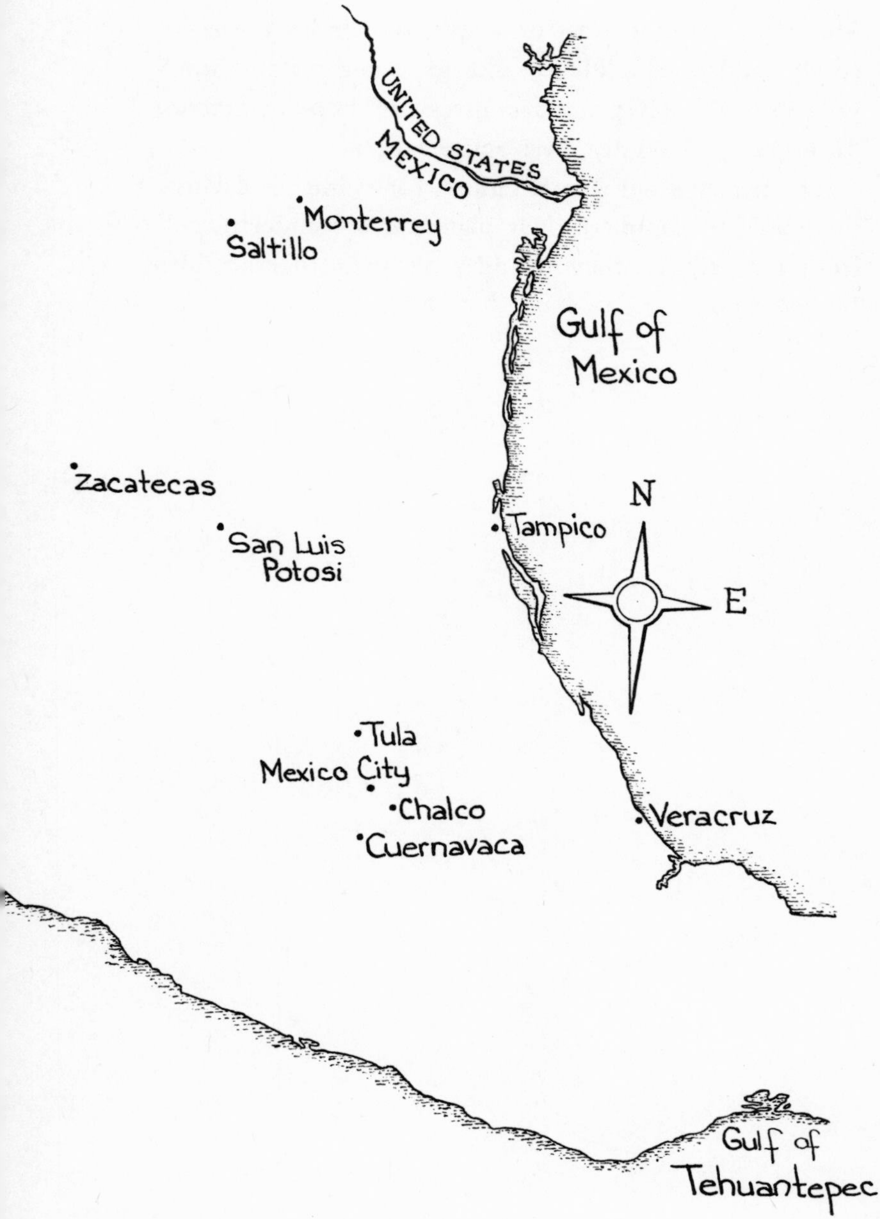
UNITED STATES
MEXICO
Monterrey
Saltillo
Gulf of Mexico
Zacatecas
N
Tampico
San Luis Potosi
E
Tula
Mexico City
Chalco
Veracruz
Cuernavaca
Gulf of Tehuantepec

15

Mexican Discoveries

Back in Washington, D.C., Edward Palmer grew more and more impatient as December of 1877 drew near. Once plans for a new trip had been completed, he could never wait to get started. What a trip this one would be — to Mexico for an entire year! Only one small worry clouded his excitement. He could not help but wonder how it would be having a partner. Perhaps thoughts of Elliott Coues's unfortunate handling of his early Arizona plants still troubled Palmer's memory. All of the expeditions that followed had been on his own or with a helper, never with an equal. Parry was, in fact, more than an equal. He was a trained botanist and taxonomist who could identify and name plants, as well as collect them.

There was nothing to do but start out and hope for

the best. After all, the trip would have been impossible without Parry's aid. To raise the one thousand dollars needed for their expenses, he had obtained funds from several botanists who would be repaid with the Mexican plants they collected. Palmer had a part of his expenses paid by the Peabody Museum of American Archaeology and Ethnology, which hired him again to investigate mounds and Indian ruins just as he had in Utah.

At last the December departure date arrived and Palmer boarded the east-coast steamer *City of New York*, bound for Veracruz, Mexico. Across the country, Parry was making his way south from his home in Davenport, Iowa, toward their meeting in Mexico City.

Upon his arival in Veracruz on December 21, Palmer took the train up to Mexico City. Parry joined him there on January 4, 1878, and together they traveled by stagecoach north to San Luis Potosí. This was the city they had previously agreed upon for their permanent headquarters. It was also decided that Parry would handle all of the plant collecting while Palmer explored Indian ruins.

Both Europe and America were just beginning to realize what a treasure chest of ruins Mexico and Central America contained. John L. Stephen's book *Incidents of Travel in Central America* started it all in 1841 by making the general public aware of the wondrous pyramids and temples left behind by a vanished American civilization. Before this the accent had been on Egypt and the Mediterranean region. Then Count Waldeck aroused tremendous public interest in Mexican ruins when his illustrated account of the hidden Mayan jungle city of

Palenque came out in 1866. He believed its builders to be descendants of the ancient Egyptians.

By the 1870s private museums and national governments eagerly sought more lost cities, temples, pyramids, and graves. The entire western world was agog with interest in the ruins of ancient empires, especially if a vanished people were involved. The government of Mexico was too absorbed in its own turbulent history to care. So men like Edward Palmer poked and pried into Mexico's thousands of burial caves and temple mounds, shipping home case after case of priceless relics.

The two collectors arrived at San Luis Potosí toward the end of January after a four-day trip from Mexico City. Center of one of Mexico's richest mining regions, San Luis Potosí was an old Spanish colonial city full of tile-domed churches, plazas, and arcades. It was situated on an arid plateau dotted with cactuses and century plants. Palmer eyed the flora with interest, but knew he would have to restrain himself and concentrate on Indians ruins this time.

His primary purpose for coming to San Luis Potosí was, after all, to investigate its Indian mounds. He had already made arrangements with a local resident, Dr. Barroeta, who would assist him. In less than a month the two of them uncovered mound relics enough to fill two bales and three large boxes. Palmer sent these over to the port of Tampico on the Gulf coast to be shipped to the Peabody Museum.

His mound digging around San Luis Potosí being finished, he turned to bird collecting and soon had 150 specimens. Next, he began a series of month-long trips into the surrounding regions. Parry stayed behind to collect plants.

One trip took Palmer to the mining city of Zacatecas to examine a nearby ruin. The mule-drawn coach he rode left San Luis Potosí at four A.M. It was a two-day journey, with time out for a quick look at a silver mine along the way.

The houses of Zacatecas seemed to be piled one on top of the other in a deep ravine hemmed in by mountains. The stone stairs leading up to the steep slopes and the arched bridges of a crumbling Spanish aqueduct gave Zacatecas a medieval air like some old European town. But he was disappointed in the ruins. They had been too badly mutilated to be of much value. He returned to San Luis Potosí with hardly enough material to pay him for his effort.

Next, he was off to Mexico City to investigate more ruins. He had planned it as a short trip, but his old enemy malaria struck him down again, keeping him there for two long months. Yet somehow he managed a trip by canal across the valley to Chalco, one out to the world-famous Pyramid of the Sun, and another over and down the mountains to Cuernavaca, always collecting wherever he could.

Meanwhile, Parry busied himself collecting plants around San Luis Potosí. But he was not happy. Perhaps the hot dry weather got on his nerves. Even Palmer's return from Mexico City in July failed to cheer him. He could have asked Palmer to help with the plants, but he did not particularly like his way of doing things. He called Palmer "industrious" but not "enterprising." Finally in August, Parry decided to return home to Iowa by Mexican cart train. He had collected only two hundred kinds of plants.

His meager collection hardly satisfied his partner. After Parry's departure Palmer really went to work. For the next three months he scoured the deserts and ranged the rich oak forests of nearby mountains, collecting eight hundred additional plants. Wherever he came across Indian ruins or villages, he also added to his artifact collection.

Yellow fever raging in the lowlands around Tampico kept Palmer in the high valleys until November 1878. Then he and a servant boarded a train of five mule carts to return to the coast. It was a rough trip but they could rest at night at the various haciendas along the way. That is, until the driver of the mule train refused to take them any further. He had arrived at his own home and decided not to go on, in spite of the fact that Palmer had contracted for his services as far as Tula. Muleback was the only means of crossing the desert plain ahead, so Palmer and his servant mounted up and set off. At Tula, Palmer was lured into the mountains by more Indian villages. Then on to the famous waterfall at El Salto, aboard an empty mule pack-train.

Whenever he went, Palmer never missed a chance to visit every famous site within reach, whether scientific, historical, or just plain interesting. His personal collections from such attractions filled trunks and boxes over the years with everything from newspaper clippings, photos, and ticket stubs to chips off famous buildings and statues. Collecting had become more than a profession to Edward Palmer. It was his life.

Two horses carried Palmer and his servant this final leg of their journey down to the river-boat landing which would take them to Tampico. From there he sailed back to New York and finally to Washington, D.C., always his temporary home between collecting trips.

American botany would long be indebted to Parry and Palmer for their efforts — one of the most important collecting trips ever made into central Mexico. Their one thousand plants included many species that were never again reported from that area.

But Palmer was far from satisfied. Parry had handled the collection in his own way, not as they had agreed. It convinced Palmer more than ever to continue working on his own, not with a partner.

In two months he was ready to set out out again — and this time alone — to collect Indian material in Texas and northern Mexico for the Peabody Museum. Since he never limited his collecting to one type of material, he had great hopes for returning with another outstanding Mexican plant collection, as well. Instead, it was a little black bug that would bring Edward Palmer as much fame as any of his plants.

He made San Antonio, Texas, his headquarters and proceeded to explore much of east Texas. Not by stage or mule or foot this time, but by rail, an almost unheard-of luxury for Palmer. As representative of the museum he was able to ride any train on a pass, and Texas of 1879 was crisscrossed with railroads.

Not so northern Mexico. When he was ready to leave for Monterrey, he found there was not even so much as a stagecoach line. He finally arranged with several other travelers to hire a private coach which would take more than two weeks to carry them on a wild trip south.

In Monterrey he gathered six boxes of pressed plants for Harvard, a box of live plants for the Department of Agriculture, and one of live plants for Dr. Engelmann. Best of all, he discovered the Mexican town markets. Past stalls of pottery and serapes, sandals and shawls, he pushed his way to the food section. Here were plants galore — not just the tropical fruits and vegetables from home plots, but all of the strange herbs and wild flowers used by the common people as medicines.

Spring in the mountains drew Palmer fifty miles west of Monterrey to Saltillo in Coahuila state, where he spent days among the pines and oaks of the highlands. The cactus-covered valleys added more choice plants to his swelling collection. Then, after exploring ancient burial caves in the western part of the state, he moved north of Saltillo to Monclova for a month. More burial caves and many new plants kept him occupied, but not too busy to be aware of the local trouble brewing around him.

The cotton growers of the rich farmlands were beginning to be desperate. A strange and terrible blight was spreading like wildfire through the district, destroying up to ninety percent of their crops. Palmer examined the cause of their trouble: a small dark-colored weevil. He collected several specimens and sent them at once to the United States Department of Agriculture along with a report of the damage they were causing in Mexico.

The insect could not be identified offhand. No one in the Department had ever seen one, nor was there an example among their insect collections. Dr. Palmer's alarm over cotton damage in distant Mexico by some unknown insect could hardly be taken seriously in

Boll weevil, Anthonomus grandis

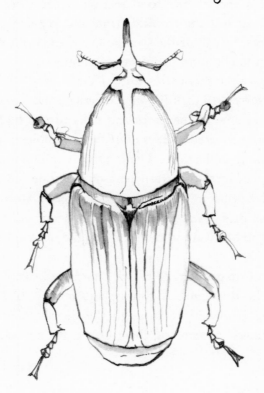

Washington. Still, the Department began sending the bug to various experts in America and Europe for identification.

Finally in Paris the weevil was identified as *Anthonomus grandis* (no common name was given). It had first been collected in Veracruz, Mexico, in 1843. A second specimen had come from Cuba in 1871. That was all the world knew about the little pest until Palmer ran across it in his 1880 explorations.

But his warning went unheeded, and by 1894 the bug was firmly entrenched over the border in Texas. One cotton grower in Corpus Christi complained to the Department:

> The "Top" crop of cotton of this section has been
> very much damaged and in some cases almost destroyed
> by a peculiar weevil or bug which by some means
> destroys the squares and small bolls. Our farmers can
> combat the cotton worm but are at a loss to know what
> to do to overcome this pest. They claim the ordinary
> methods of poisoning for cotton worm have no effect on
> these bugs . . . (From *Smithsonian Miscellaneous
> Collections*, 1930)

In 1903 the insect crossed over into Louisiana. There was some effort to stop the spread but it came too late. By 1907 it had entered Mississippi and most of the Deep South.

Now it was no longer a strange insect without a name, for Edward Palmer had stumbled upon the dreaded cotton boll weevil, the insect which would ruin much of the South's cotton as well as its economy before it could finally be controlled.

Palmer's little black bug invaded not only the cotton

fields but also the folk tales, the jokes, the political cartoons, and the songs of the South. How Palmer must have sighed with a grim I-told-you-so in his later years whenever he heard the famous work song of the Texas Negroes:

The boll weevil sez to the farmer,
"What make yo' neck so red?"
"Tryin' to beat you devils;
It's a wonder I ain't dead,"
For you're takin' my home, Babe, just a-takin' my home!"

"Well ef you want to kill us,
I'll sho-God tell yo' how,
Just bundle up yo' cotton sack
And th'ow away yo' plow,
Then hunt yo' a home, Babe, then hunt yo' a home!"
(From *Smithsonian Miscellaneous Collections*, 1930)

16

Mounds and Grass

Of all the mysterious relics of early peoples of America, none were stranger than the man-made mounds of the eastern United States. In the West it was clear there were Indians around who could still erect remarkable pueblos. In Mexico the great building skill of the Aztecs and Mayas was a matter of history. But who could have made the eastern mounds?

Early American colonists first discovered the mounds when they began clearing land for settlements. They called them "tumuli" or "barrows." Such earth heaps came in all shapes and sizes, and could be found from Canada to the tip of Florida. Thousands lined great river valleys like the Mississippi and Ohio.

The mounds were small and round . . . large and round . . . large and flat-topped . . . pyramid-shaped . . . in squares and circles...shaped like eagles and snakes. They stood alone or in large or small groups. One of the largest was 1,000 feet long, 700 feet wide, and 100 feet high. It may have taken 100,000 men more than twenty years to build it by hauling dirt in baskets.

Thomas Jefferson was one of the first Americans to examine these earth heaps. He dug into mounds on his own property in Virginia, found bones, beads, and arrowheads, and concluded they were Indian burials. William Henry Harrison was another president fascinated by the mound mystery. From his evidence he decided they were the work of the Aztecs of Mexico. Dozens of ordinary farmers and amateur archaeologists began digging up mounds for the sole purpose of retrieving buried relics. By Civil War days vast private collections had been built up, and every town had its dealer in "Indian relics."

Who had built the mounds? Certainly not the primitive woodland Indians. Scientists of Palmer's day ruled them out from the start. Besides, the Indians themselves disclaimed any connection with the mounds. Nineteenth-century scholars had no idea, at that time, how long Indians had lived on the American continent, so they focussed their theories on an earlier, more highly civilized race of people who must have preceded the Indians and then vanished from the scene.

Some said the Mound Builders had come from ancient Babylon or Egypt. A favorite theory during the 1880s pointed to the Ten Lost Tribes of Israel. In 1879 the Smithsonian Institution set up a Bureau of American

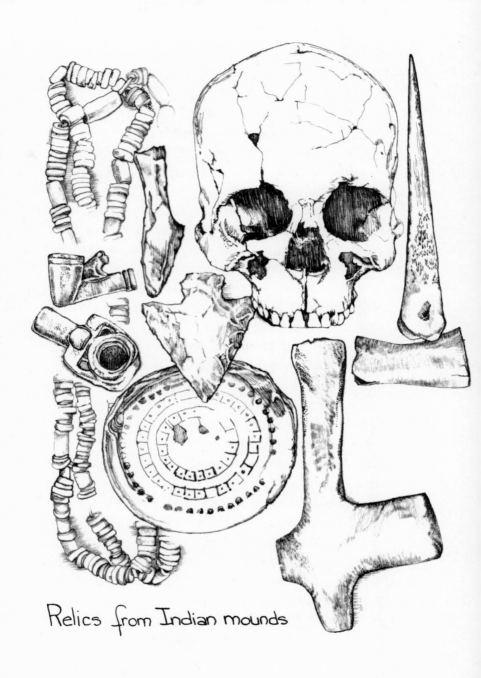

Relics from Indian mounds

Ethnology to look into such matters. Government mound-exploration began in 1881 under the direction of Cyrus Thomas.

Edward Palmer was in Washington at the time, and his long-time sponsor, Professor Baird, saw to it that he got in on the work from the start. He was appointed field worker for the Bureau at a salary of $125 a month for the next three years.

It was Palmer's job to track down and make a survey of all known mounds. Wherever mound relics were reported, he would hurry to the spot to locate any mounds in the vicinity. Whenever he heard of "mound pottery" being sold, he would try to trace it back to its origin. If possible, he would dig into the mounds and ship any relics he found back to the Bureau.

For the first year he spent most of his time exploring mounds in Tennessee and Arkansas. The excavation of the McMahan Mound near Sevierville, Tennessee, is a typical example of his work. Palmer knew before he arrived that the owners of the land had been refusing to have the mound opened for years. Still he spent several days trying to change their minds. He was about to leave when they suddenly yielded.

He began measuring and digging at once. The mound was 16 feet high and 240 feet around. Three feet beneath the surface he came to burnt clay, part of a roof of what seemed to be a log tomb. Next there were remains of cedar posts, then ashes. At the four-foot depth were pieces of articles. Then came four and a half more feet of dirt, many skeletons, ashes for two feet, and finally red clay. Three feet below this was undisturbed soil.

From the mound he collected two boxes of human bones, twenty skulls, arrowheads, hammerstones, stone and clay pipes, quartz game pebbles, glass beads, shells, and pottery. The shell ornaments he found were the most remarkable collection yet discovered. They included clamshells with rattlesnake designs, a shell mask, and an engraved shell showing two fighting figures. Palmer identified ten different species of shells among the beads, tools, and ornaments. It was evident to him that this was a burial mound with bodies and grave relics similar to those he had uncovered in Utah and Mexico.

Most important of all, he discovered a pair of brass pins — of European make — which had been buried with the bodies. Not only Palmer but all of the field workers came up with such positive proof that some of the mounds had been built *after* the white man's appearance. The only people in the area at that time were the woodland Indians. They must have been the builders.

Still, it was hard for the average person, or even for a scientist, to give up the romantic idea of an ancient, non-Indian race in America. They would look at the poor reservation Indians and shake their heads. So Palmer and the Bureau of Ethnology continued their work year after year.

Many of the mounds rose from the bluffs along the Mississippi River flood plain. Palmer examined those in the Arkansas bayou country until winter rains nearly washed him away. When weather permitted, he began again, first in eastern Tennessee, then in Missouri. During the summer of 1882 he excavated mounds around Vincennes, Indiana. He spent the fall and winter back in Arkansas, following that trip with a series of shorter visits to mounds in Louisiana, Mississippi, Alabama, and Tennessee. The autumn of 1883 Palmer spent in central Arkansas. He visited shell mounds at Huntsville, Alabama, during the winter, and investigated Georgia and South Carolina mounds in the spring of 1884.

The mound investigation begun by men like Palmer was only the groundwork for studies that would continue up to the present day. It was obvious to Palmer, from his previous experience in the Southwest and Mexico, that the eastern mounds had indeed been constructed by Indians. What Indians and when were the questions he could not begin to answer. Even the leading experts were confounded by the results of the Bureau's survey. Field workers like Palmer had located over one million mounds. The number of different kinds and the variety of their contents only did more to confuse the issue.

The solution to the mystery of the eastern mounds was not a simple one. Pieces of the puzzle are still missing today. But in the years to come, archaeologists would unravel much of the long, complex tale. Today we know that the mounds were made by eastern Indians, but not by a single tribe. Certain groups built mounds. Others did not. Nor were they all made at the same time.

As early as 4000 B.C. a hunting, shellfish-eating people occupied sites along rivers and coasts, letting their shells accumulate over hundreds of years until huge shell mounds were formed. They lived in shelters on top of these mounds generation after generation, burying their dead within them.

Then around A.D. 500 a new wave of Indians migrated to the East, bringing with them the cultivation of corn and their custom of burying their chiefs in specially built earthern mounds. Large villages grew up around such burial mounds. In the centuries to come, eastern Indian civilization rose to new heights, climaxed by the building of great flat-topped temple mounds on which religious ceremonies were held.

Then in the 1500s and 1600s, mound building ceased altogether and was eventually forgotten by the Indians. The reasons are not clear. Defeat by more aggressive primitive tribes and the coming of the white man are the most logical explanations. Spanish explorers of the 1500s such as Cabeza de Vaca, Hernando de Soto, and Tristán de Luna actually witnessed eastern Indians building mounds. Such observations in their journals were dismissed by the nineteenth-century scholars as false reports. It was not until modern times that scientists were able to date the mounds with radioactive carbon, and prove the truth of the Spanish claims.

Edward Palmer's three years of mound work received almost as little notice as the Spanish records. His name is mentioned only occasionally in the Bureau reports, and much of his field work as well as the two thousand specimens he collected is not credited to his name. The reason for this is now unknown — only that Palmer complained of unfair treatment at the hands of the Bureau.

When his third season of work was completed, Palmer turned west again. All this while, plant collecting had seemed almost forgotten. But it was always his first love, and he returned to it in the winter of 1884. Back to the Southwest he went, all the way to Yuma, Arizona, by train. For years he had kept in the back of his mind a picture of the curious Cocopa Indians. They lived at the mouth of the Colorado River in Mexico and regulated their lives by the rise and fall of the ocean tides sweeping inland from the Gulf of California. They grew no crops, but depended entirely upon the wild plants around them. Palmer especially remembered the wild grass they harvested each year, and was determined to collect some.

The coming of the railroad to Yuma had spelled the end of steamboating on the Colorado. Old stern-wheelers like the *Cocopah* which Palmer had ridden fifteen years earlier were long gone. Even the shipyard down at Puerto Isabel, Mexico, had been torn down.

But Palmer's determination had not brought him all the way across the country for nothing. He rounded up an interested group of travelers to share the expenses of a wagon down to Puerto Isabel. There he hired a boat for the short trip out to the Great Horseshoe Bend of the river where the Cocopa's "grass camp" was located.

The grass was there, all right, but no camp nor Indians. It seems that their camp was set up only during the April harvest. Being completely out of flower at this time, the grass was also worthless to Palmer as a specimen. But he would be back. This was his third trip to the area. It would take two more before he finally found the Cocopas at home.

Two men from the United States Fish Commission accompanied Palmer on his final trip in 1889. The grass harvest was in progress when they arrived. It was a sight to behold.

From the grass camp on high ground to the mouth of the river twelve miles away was one great sea of Indian grass, spreading out for perhaps twenty miles on either side of the river. The grass itself was two to four feet high and covered from top to bottom with stiff sharp leaves. At the top of each stem was a tightly packed head of ripe seeds. The entire crop had been planted by nature and watered automatically by the daily overflow of tides. Palmer knew that few man-made grain fields could equal this amazing spread.

As soon as the tidal waters had drained off into the river, the Indians hurried into the grass fields. They worked swiftly in a race with the waters that would soon return and force them back to higher ground. The grass stems were brittle enough to be sliced off, but any movement at all was difficult. At every step the Indians sank to their knees in the soft, gluey clay. Also, the spiny leaves of the grass soon covered their arms and legs with painful scratches.

When the tide returned, they trudged back to camp with their bundles of grain. Huge fires were started to dry out the grain heads. These were then threshed with a stick. Last of all, the separate kernels were shelled by being trampled under the Indian's leathery feet.

Palmer's joy at finally witnessing the whole process was complete when he later learned that the Cocopa grass was new to science and would be named for him: *Uniola palmeri*.

Several other Cocopa foods attracted him. One was the common cattail. Its roots were a great favorite of these Indians, and were always chewed before long desert journeys to prevent thirst. Another was the strange orange sand-food plant. It grew completely buried in desert sand up to its woolly head. Its boiled or roasted roots tasted like sweet potatoes, Palmer claimed. When raw, its roots were a welcome source of water to desert Indians.

Like the grass harvest in spring, the harvest of wild piñon nuts in fall supplied the Cocopas with the rest of their basic diet. Palmer had great admiration for a people who could turn the products of nature into such delicious foods. He happened to run across a party of them gathering their yearly supply of nuts along the Mexican border one season, and was so impressed that he wrote:

> It was an interesting sight to see these children of nature with their dirty laughing faces, parching and eating the pine nuts. They had already filled many bags and were eating them by the handfuls. Indeed we found the piñones to be rich and well-flavored, and we were not satisfied with few. We realized that these happy free people were in their natural habitat here beneath the pines. At last we had the privilege of seeing primitive Americans gathering their uncultivated crop from primaeval groves.
> (Reprinted courtesy of *Popular Science Monthly*, © 1911 by The Science Press)

17

Mexican Travels

After each of his trips, Edward Palmer always returned to Washington, D.C., in hopes that Professor
Baird at the Smithsonian might have a new collecting
task lined up for him. In 1885 a particularly enjoyable
assignment awaited him. The Smithsonian asked him to
undertake a study of the little-known Tarahumara Indians in the Mexican state of Chihuahua.

The southwestern United States had once been Palmer's favorite collecting grounds. But now the lure of
Mexico was growing stronger. It had many more of the
wild and remote corners he especially relished, strange
out-of-the-way spots hardly touched by the white man.

Palmer journeyed south to the border at El Paso,
Texas, by train. Railroads had entered Mexico as well,
and he was able to cross the entire state of Chihuahua

— Mexico's largest — by rail. The tracks ran across desert and plateau grazing lands to Chihuahua city, capital of the state, then on into hilly and finally mountainous desert country. At Jiménez, Palmer boarded the stagecoach for a brief ride west to Parral, the end of the line and the beginning of the rugged silver-mining region which was his goal.

His destination was Hacienda San Miguel, home of A. R. Shepherd, owner of the silver mines near the town of Batopilas. It was a rough six-day trip by muleback over the mountains to the hacienda. But the fifty-four-year-old Palmer took it in his usual stride. He journeyed from water hole to water hole till he reached the eastern edge of the Sierra Madre Occidental range. Then, up the dry rocky slopes to the forested summit. A winding road through a mountain ravine finally led him down to the hacienda.

Mr. Shepherd had been a former governor of the District of Columbia and an acquaintance of Professor Baird. The professor had arranged with him for Palmer's stay. Palmer spent the summer collecting plants. Although his assignment did not include plant collecting, he could hardly pass up the flora of such a little-known region. Even the trees and shrubs around the ranch buildings were strange to him.

One was the pricklenut or Mexican elm. It grew wild along dry washes and was transplanted to provide shade around the hacienda. It was a medium-sized tree with elmlike leaves and prickly black nuts. The people of Mexico, like those of Paraguay, used such trees in many ways. Spoons were carved out of the pricklenut's soft

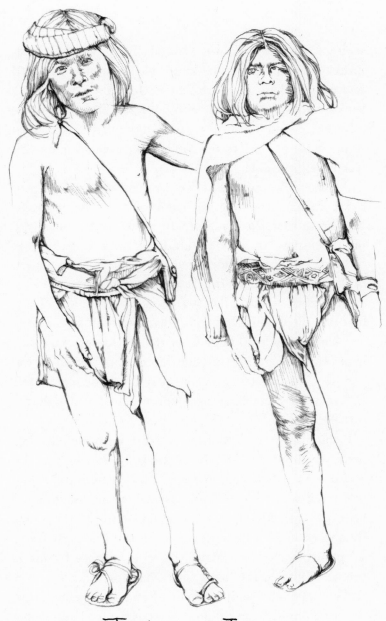

Tarahumara Indian

white wood. Its bark was twisted into rope and its nut meats ground up for making cakes. Palmer gathered samples of these products, as well as the pricklenut's leaves, bark, and nuts. He also collected along the Batopilas River, but found the going difficult because steep slopes came so close to the stream that even a mule track was barely possible.

As the fall approached, he worked his way up into the mountains, reaching the height of 8,850 feet in October. From there he traveled 150 miles north, still in the high country, to visit the Indians he was seeking at Norogachi village. They lived at 8,500 feet in a rough, broken region full of ridges and ravines surrounded by even higher peaks. Like the Incas of Peru, the Tarahumaras were noted for their amazing endurance. Other Mexicans considered them to be the world's greatest runners. Tarahumara men thought nothing of hiking all the way to Chihuahua city, where they could be seen in the streets with their long hair, short pants, and colorful turbans.

Palmer spent two months at their village, collecting over six hundred pounds of Indian artifacts for the Smithsonian. The clay pottery they produced greatly interested him. No detail of its making or use escaped his eagle eye. He even went so far as to list their uses for pieces of broken pottery: to hold portions of food; as spoons; to hold ointment; to remove ashes from the fire or dirt from the house; as covers for other pots; on roofs during the summer to hold and dry beans, corn, watermelon seeds, and pumpkin seeds; to feed and water chickens and dogs; to store salt, red pepper, dried meat, roots, berries, seeds, old buttons, nails, and dyes in primitive cupboards of lashed sticks; to shape and smooth new pots; to stand new pots on while they were drying. Finally, large pieces were inverted over the hearth ashes at night to preserve the fire. To Edward Palmer, the great collector, here was a people after his own heart.

When he returned to the United States in December, Palmer carried with him the most important collection of plants and artifacts ever to come from this region.

Where to go next? No assignment awaited him in Washington in 1886, so he decided to travel on his own to another unexplored region. He would pay his way by selling plants to various institutions and private collectors. Mexico still offered the best opportunity for securing new plants. He pored over maps and consulted his botanist friends before selecting the most promising location.

The city of Guadalajara in the state of Jalisco was his final choice. It lay at the rim of a deep, wild ravine gouged out by the Río Grande de Santiago. Upon his arrival, Palmer found he could live in the city and make daily collecting trips into the ravine and its several branch canyons. His plant collection for the summer soon grew to 770 different species — another outstanding series.

Almost as valuable was his pottery collection. Guadalajara was famous throughout Mexico for its pottery. The most skillful potters were — and still are — the Indians from the nearby villages of San Pedro Tlaquepaque and Tonalá. Palmer returned with ninety pottery specimens of his own and a large collection donated by a

Guadalajara acquaintance of his. These he presented to the National Museum, a branch of the Smithsonian in Washington. His plants he sold for $900, only $200 above his expenses. All in all, Palmer considered the trip a success, and was ready to set out at once on a new one.

The Department of Agriculture's Division of Botany offered him just the sort of position he wanted: the post of field botanical collector at a salary of $100 a month plus $50 traveling expenses. He would hold this job for the next six years until 1893. It would keep him in the field for longer periods at a time than any collecting he had ever done. It would send him back and forth across the United States and into Mexico so many times that he could have filled a thick travel book with his experiences.

The Department was especially interested in building up the National Herbarium into a complete reference collection. It needed many more pressed plant specimens. Palmer spent most of 1887 around Guaymas, Mexico, on the Gulf of California, crossing over to the Baja peninsula twice in his search for such plants.

In 1888 he moved to California for plant collecting, as well as photographing certain features of California's vegetation, at the Department's request. He had often taken pictures on his other trips, but this was his first paid assignment. Photography was a natural outgrowth of his work, for it made his descriptions of plants and their growing locations more accurate. Pencil sketches were another means he used to supplement his field notes when he had time.

Plant exploring on Mount Whitney, then the highest

mountain in the United States, had long been one of Palmer's dreams. Here was another out-of-the-way spot which few botanists had ever visited. This seemed an ideal time to do it. First of all, he contacted William G. Wright, an old acquaintance at San Bernardino. The two of them decided to attempt the trip together. They set out for the central California Sierra country by rail the first of June as far as the train would take them. From Caliente, the last stop, they took the stagecoach to Kernville, nearest town to the mountain. It was an old mining town, which Palmer called "a whisky-blighted place." Unfortunately, snow still remained in the mountains and they were forced to postpone their trip.

Palmer tried again in July. This time he hired a guide in Kernville to take him through the rugged high Sierra country to Mount Whitney. Palmer realized something was wrong from the very start, but it wasn't until the third day that the reason became clear. The guide refused to go any further. He finally admitted that the country was completely unfamiliar to him. He had not known where he was going from the beginning. By this time supplies were low, and it was all they could do to reach Kernville again. Palmer's plans to climb Mount Whitney had to be abandoned — this time permanently.

The year 1889 was not a good one for Edward Palmer. He remained in California, at San Diego, collecting whenever possible, but his health was poor. In June a respiratory infection interfered with plans for a trip into Baja. At the end of the month he was hospitalized briefly by an "enlargement of the liver." In November he returned to the hospital again for an abdominal operation. But by December he seemed fully recovered, enough for an extended trip into Mexico.

He visited five western Mexican states, stopping at every important city and journeying into the unexplored wilderness wherever possible. The plant collection which he assembled from 1888 till 1892 numbered 2,780 species, the longest series of his career.

Even though he was conditioned for such trips, they must have been a strain on a man of sixty. Yet never once did he consider slowing his pace or discontinuing his search for new plants. Perhaps his amazing stamina was due in part to some of the energy-giving plant foods he ate. In wilderness areas he followed the habits of the Indians, often becoming quite fond of their foods. One, so important to him that he published an article about it, was *chia*, made from seeds of the desert sage, a species of *Salvia*.

It was said that one teaspoonful of *chia* could sustain an Indian on a twenty-four-hour hike. Aware of its high energy value, Mexicans, and many American residents of the Southwest also, roasted, ground, and prepared its seeds like cereal. Said Palmer:

> As a food both nutritious and palatable it deserves to be better known. The white races are, perhaps, too apt to look with contempt upon the contents of the Indian granary, and though Chia is never likely to take rank as one of the great staples, it may come to be as universally esteemed among the civilized as it is among the aborigines of the region where it grows.
> (From *Zoe*, July, 1891)

Palmer carried *chia* with him whenever he could obtain the seeds. It grew wild so abundantly in parts of California and Mexico that it was threshed like grain and sold in markets and drugstores. Not only did he pack it with him on trips, but he also enjoyed its refreshing properties in lemonade on hot summer days, or as a health restorer when he was sick. According to Palmer, "it is easily borne by the most delicate stomach, and at the same time affords considerable nutrition."

A new interest in this high-energy plant food has recently appeared in the modern Southwest.

One interesting side trip Palmer made in 1890 took him to Fort Apache in Arizona's White Mountains. He was amazed at the changes that had taken place since his last encounter with the Apache Indians. Many were now peaceful farmers, growing hay and corn on their reservation land. He could hardly believe that these were the fierce fighters who had so recently scorned the raising of crops as women's work.

Some of the men were employed at the fort as scouts to help the army locate the last of the renegade Apache bands in Arizona. Palmer talked with these now civilized Apaches and was appalled to find how much like the white man they had already become. One scout called "Riley" told him:

> Fort Apache is dull. I want to go to Holbrook and
> be cow-puncher; then I can go to the bar, like other men
> and say "Boys, come up and take a drink."
> (From *Zoe*, March, 1890)

Yet certain Indian customs would never change. One was the "mother-in-law taboo." No Apache man was allowed to speak to or even go near his wife's mother.

Officers at the fort learned this the hard way when they put on a huge Christmas dinner for the Indian scouts and their families. All of the relatives showed up, but none of the scouts! They did not dare to appear in the presence of their mothers-in-law.

Palmer's final season of work for the Department of Agriculture's Division of Botany was in 1893, when he made an extensive plant survey of the Snake River plains in southern Idaho. After this he decided to maintain a permanent home in Washington, D.C. It would place him in close contact with the important government centers of botanical interest. He would be on hand for any new expeditions or plant surveys that might be undertaken. And by now he had more acquaintances in Washington than in any other city.

Yet 1894 brought no new government-sponsored opportunities, so Palmer decided to go to Mexico on his own. This time he crossed the United States to San Francisco and then continued by steamer down to Acapulco, in those days a tiny fishing village on Mexico's west coast. He had stopped there many years before while en route to Panama, but not long enough to collect plants.

He made the Hotel del Pacifico his headquarters, and was surprised to meet another American guest, Major Edward A. Goldman, who was there to collect animals. The two of them decided to combine their efforts and were soon making short horseback trips into the hills together. In later years Major Goldman remembered Palmer as an old man with thick white hair and a drooping mustache who was not strong but very active. He would work for long hours pressing his plants and changing the blotters. But he also talked and even joked with the other hotel guests. He was sixty-three at the time, and perhaps the years had somewhat mellowed his overserious nature.

At Acapulco he collected 635 different kinds of plants. It should be noted that here, as in every collection Palmer made, he gathered duplicates of every species in order to supply as many complete sets of his plants as possible to the various buyers. Altogether he collected five thousand specimens of the 635 species at Acapulco.

The amount of work involved in preparing such a large collection is hard to imagine. Each plant had to be flattened, screwed down, and pressed between blotters in a plant press. To insure proper drying, the blotters had to be changed again and again. No wonder Major Goldman was impressed with the long and late hours Palmer spent working over his plants at the hotel.

Yet from the beginning — from his first expedition to Paraguay — Edward Palmer knew that a collector's life was, in the long run, an exacting one. The actual exploring of strange and wildly beautiful lands might be exciting, but this was a minor part of his work. Palmer spent the major portion of every trip in cramped dispensary huts or rickety leantos or damp dugouts or musty hotel rooms, preparing his specimens. This was the price he had to pay for the glamour of the trip and the glory of new discoveries — and he was always willing.

Again at Acapulco, a good many of his plants were

new to science. Some named for him included a yellow sapote, *Lucuma palmeri*, one of the wild tropical fruits of the region; a morning-glory, *Ipomoea palmeri*, which he found in a high valley among the seaside mountains; and a large shrub with white flowers, *Montanoa palmeri*, which covered the hillsides and smelled like apple blossoms.

After his return to Washington early in 1895, Palmer rested for more than a year before attempting a new trip, again to Mexico and again on his own. This time he made the city of Durango his headquarters. Between March and mid-November he collected eight thousand plants of 974 species.

In May of 1897 the Department of Agriculture hired Palmer to make a report on the timber trees of Mexico whose wood was imported into the United States, and on Mexican trees which grew successfully in arid regions. It was a large order, but he started out in good spirits, glad to be working for a government agency again. Although they sometimes mishandled his collections, still it was better to be the scientific representative of a United States government agency than merely a private citizen in a foreign country.

The western cities of Mexico — Nogales, Guaymas, Culiacán, Mazatlán, Manzanillo, and Colima — were his headquarters. From them he rode out on horseback, muleback, or wagon, taking samples of timber trees, jotting down descriptions, and, as always, collecting plants. At Guaymas and again at Colima he suffered renewed attacks of malaria. Yet he would remember these cities for their wonderful outdoor markets, not for his fever.

Indians from the surrounding countryside would come into town at daybreak, setting up shop on mats on the ground. Neat stacks of pottery, baskets, tropical fruits, and sugar cane soon lined the market square. Palmer was impressed by vendors like the *tuberos* with their strange ringing cries and large gourds full of *tuba*, or coconut toddy, dangling from either end of a carrying pole. A small drinking gourd hung from a string around their waists. The charge was two centavos for a gourdful of *tuba*. Palmer sampled this as he did every native food and drink, but the fermented coconut flavor of the palm sap only made him sick.

Yet the next year of 1898 found him in Mexico again. Most of his plants this time came from the fascinating city markets of Saltillo, San Luis Potosí, Parras, and Torreón. At Zacatecas a serious case of pneumonia ended his collecting for the season with six thousand plants — 814 different kinds. This attack slowed him down considerably. He spent the year 1899 recuperating in Washington with only one brief collecting trip — to Mammoth Cave in Kentucky.

In July the Department of Agriculture again needed Palmer's assistance. His own collections and field notes, which had swelled to great proportions during the past few years, needed someone to sort them over and straighten them out. The collector himself was hired for the task. It pleased him mightily to work again with his precious plants from the distant states of Mexico. Each one carried memories of the time and place and difficulties of its collection. If he could not travel there himself, at least he could look at his plants and remember. Palmer remained in Washington at this job until 1902 — the longest he had ever been away from collecting.

Although he was now seventy-one, the thought of giving up field trips never entered Palmer's mind. When he heard of a proposed collecting trip to Cuba for the National Museum, he was all set to go. Had Professor Baird been alive, he would have hired Palmer on the spot. But this staunchest of Palmer's supporters had died in 1888. Now the museum turned to younger men for its collecting chores. Botanist Charles L. Pollard, aged thirty, and taxidermist William Palmer (no relation), forty-six, were hired for the expedition. Very well, then Edward Palmer would volunteer to go for nothing. The younger men agreed, and soon the three of them were off for six wonderful weeks of collecting plants, birds, bats, insects, and marine life in eastern Cuba.

Palmer rounded out the year in Mexico again. He returned to San Luis Potosí with visions of accomplishing a favorite idea of his: the canning of fruits and sap of the edible cactuses. The round red fruits of the prickly pear called *tunas* were a staple food throughout Mexico. Palmer had watched daily burro-loads of *tunas* heading for every town market during the summer. A sweet sap called *agua miel*, sucked from the hearts of certain century plants, was another important product. What a boon to Mexico if these foods could be canned when they were in season and preserved until winter! Palmer spent a month of his time and a hundred dollars from his pocket trying to can them. But the jars kept bursting their seals, and in the end he was forced to give up.

Upon his return from Mexico, Palmer settled down in Washington for another long stay. He had been hired again by the Department of Agriculture to continue work on his specimens and notes, which he did until 1905. The job was terminated at his own request when he could no longer resist the lure of Mexico. He set out for San Luis Potosí again to spend the season gathering fruits and economic plants in the town markets.

His collection of 1906 was even more remarkable. Palmer was seventy-five when he left for the state of Durango in western Mexico. He took the train from Durango city to the end of the line and then continued on to the wild northwest corner of the state "to see what is there." He had been invited into the mountains by a mine owner. The trip involved making a difficult eight-day ride by horseback up to the mine at eight thousand feet and back. In the mountains he collected the wonderful spring flowers that appeared as the snow melted. His Durango collection has no equal. Few persons were later able to visit the remote mountains after the mines had shut down, so that his plants are among the very few ever gathered from this region.

Few men of Palmer's age would have attempted such a trip, let alone left the security of a paying job in the city to venture into a foreign land on their own. Palmer's only means of support for most of his later Mexican trips was the sale of his plant collections.

Why did he do it? Why would a man seventy-five years old, weak from lifelong attacks of malaria, why would such a man give up the long-overdue comforts of civilized life to return to the wilds?

Palmer had no choice. He had spent over fifty-five years in the field, and the hard life of the open trail was a part of him. He could not change, even had he wanted to. While he seldom made known his inner feelings on this or any other subject, in the following story about Indians Palmer seems to be describing himself as he was during his last years in Washington:

> It is a remark of military men who have been much
> with the Indians, that if they are fed much on the
> flesh and cereals and other adjuncts of the white man's
> table, they pine away and lead an abandoned and
> unhappy life, and that, confined to this fare, many
> would die as if visited by an epidemic. There is an
> unsatisfied craving within them for the rude fare of
> their wild life, for the coarse, bulky, precarious food
> of their younger days, for the messes of their tribe,
> however rude and unsavory they may appear to others.
> They hail therefore with a yell of pleasure, the
> opportunity to leap over the bounds of civilization
> into wild scenes familiar to their childhood.
> (From *Report of the Commissioner of Agriculture
> for the Year 1870*)

There were a few people in Washington at the turn of the century who could appreciate this point of view. One was Commander William E. Safford, a botanist at the Department of Agriculture. Commander Safford had been the first American vice-governor on the Pacific island of Guam after its capture during the Spanish-American War. He was fascinated by the useful plants of the island, and decided to give up his naval career to devote his life to botany.

When Palmer met him at the Department of Agriculture, Safford had already published his successful book *The Useful Plants of the Island of Guam.* He had next turned to a new and burning interest: the useful plants of Mexico. Palmer was just the man for him to know.

Safford spent many hours with the old doctor, helping him sort out his notes, reading his diaries, and listening to Palmer's tales of his remarkable adventures. He was one of the few persons of Palmer's day to learn the complete story of the great collector's life. Indeed, he was so impressed he decided to write a book about Palmer.

Safford was also delighted that Palmer could continue his field work in Mexico. It would bring in more and more material on the useful plants of that country. In 1907 Palmer left for Cuidad Victoria. His next trip, in 1908, was to Chihuahua. There he gathered seeds, fruits, corn, beans, peppers, orange blossoms (for tea), and native drugs from the city market. In 1909-10, the last collecting trip of his life took Palmer to Tampico for six months. Even at seventy-nine he was able to make field trips from there, such as his journey by schooner down to Juana Ramirez Island off the hot lowlands of Veracruz. He collected 4,400 specimens of 598 different plants on this, his last trip.

Palmer was back in Washington before his eightieth birthday in January 1911. What a surprise awaited him! The Botanical Society of Washington had planned a meeting in his honor to celebrate his birthday. A large number of botanists attended, and Commander Safford read a glowing sketch of Palmer's life. Safford describes the occasion:

> During the meeting of the society Dr. Palmer was seated in the place of honor, and at the close of the exercises he was presented with an appropriate birthday gift as a token of the appreciation of the members of the society of his important life-work. The venerable traveler received the congratulations of those present with tears streaming down his cheeks, doubtless realizing that this must be his valedictory. (From *Botanical Gazette*, July, 1911)

The honor came just in time. Three months afterwards he took to his bed with a sudden attack of pneumonia. On April 10, 1911, only a few days later, Edward Palmer was dead.

18

Forgotten Man

Surely Edward Palmer had earned the right to be remembered as one of America's greatest scientific collectors. Surely his hundreds of plant discoveries and lifetime of field work should have built him a lasting memorial in the halls of science.

He alone collected more than 100,000 plants for the museums of the world, not to mention the thousands of birds, animals, insects, shells, and Indian artifacts. Every major American scientific institution of his day benefitted from his thousands of plant collections. To name only a few: the United States National Herbarium, the New York Botanical Garden, the Gray Herbarium at Harvard, Yale University, the Academy of Natural Sciences at Philadelphia, the Chicago Natural History Museum, the Missouri Botanical Garden, Iowa State

College, and the California Academy of Sciences. His collections proved just as valuable abroad, at such institutions as the British Museum, the Royal Botanic Gardens of England, the Conservatoire et Jardin Botaniques of Switzerland, the Muséum National d'Histoire Naturelle of France, the Botanisches Museum of Germany, and the Komarov Botanical Institute of Russia.

Nearly two thousand plants entirely new to science were discovered by him. Two hundred species were named in his honor. He was the first scientist to explore Guadalupe Island, Cantillas Canyon, Lake Okeechobee, the Indian mounds of the Southwest; to warn America about the cotton boll weevil; to contribute a lifetime of work on the economic uses of plants. Surely such a man deserved to be remembered by a grateful scientific world.

He was not. He had written no books. He had left behind no descendants to preserve his memory. He was a lone wolf dedicated to plants, not to people, so he left few friends. Professor Baird, one of his greatest supporters, had passed away in 1888. Even Commander Safford, the one other person who could have preserved his memory forever, died before finishing his book on Palmer's life. Safford had written twenty-four chapters — 702 pages — and then tucked it away to gather dust in the files of the Department of Agriculture.

In his will Palmer asked that his notes and papers (nine boxes and two trunks full) be published, setting aside two thousand dollars for this purpose. They were not. Instead, the entire contents of these boxes and trunks were sold at auction and either scattered across the country or lost.

Only his plants were left. But many of these had been sorted and classified and sold by other men. More often than not, they were carelessly labeled. His careful notes about their location, growing season, color, and uses were often lost. Without such field notes to describe them, a great deal of their value was lost. Within twenty years after his death, almost nothing remained to remind the world of Edward Palmer's existence. It seemed as if the strange fate that had interfered with his accomplishments throughout his life was having one last fling.

Then, almost by accident, he was rediscovered. Rogers McVaugh, professor of botany and author of *Ferns of Georgia*, was a botanist for the Department of Agriculture in 1940. His work took him often to the National Herbarium to examine certain pressed plants. One specimen of particular interest had been collected by an Edward Palmer. No other information was given.

In his search for more facts, McVaugh ran across a complete set of the collector's notes in his own department. These had never been filed with their specimens in the Herbarium. In addition, he discovered folders full of manuscripts handwritten by Palmer himself, as well as the huge typed biography begun by Safford.

McVaugh's interest was aroused. As he read through these sources, Palmer's remarkable career began to unfold. Still, there were great gaps in the story. Perhaps other Washington institutions could help. McVaugh found that the Smithsonian was the richest source of Palmer material, with the National Archives a close second.

Tracing Palmer's life became a serious project for

McVaugh in the years to follow. He visited the biological libraries of Harvard University. He began tracking down the Palmer material sold at public auction in 1914. Of the three hundred separate lots sold, he was able to locate one-third of the manuscripts. He examined 650 letters written by Palmer during his lifetime of plant collecting. In 1951 he made an extensive tour of Mexico, following Palmer's trail wherever possible.

A detailed picture resulted, showing Palmer's collecting activities and travels over a sixty-year period. But what of the man himself? Rebuilding a personality was much more difficult. There were few living people who remembered Palmer. Most of them knew him only during his latter years as "a nice old man puttering around the Smithsonian." Palmer's letters were of little help. They rarely expressed his personal opinions.

And so he stands today, a solid enough figure from his photographs, travels, and collections, but a shadowy personality, with here and there a brush stroke added by someone like Mrs. Johnson from St. George, Utah, or Major Edwards at Acapulco, Mexico.

Professor McVaugh published his results in 1956 as *Edward Palmer, Plant Explorer of the American West.* The book included a compact biography, an index of Palmer's travels, a guide to his field notes and plant collections, and a list of Palmer sources. To the general public it made Edward Palmer real again. To the modern botanist it made possible valuable research on his neglected plant collections. And to Edward Palmer, himself, it made truly worthwhile the fulfillment of the vow he had made so long ago: "to spend my life in the prosecution of science."

BIBLIOGRAPHY

ABEL, ANNIE HELOISE. *The American Indian as Participant in the Civil War.* Cleveland, The Arthur H. Clark Co., 1919.

HIBBEN, FRANK C. *Digging Up America.* New York, Hill & Wang, Inc., 1960.

KEARNEY, THOMAS H., and PEEBLES, ROBERT H. *Arizona Flora.* Berkeley, University of California Press, 1960.

LOCKWOOD, FRANK C. *The Apache Indians.* New York, The Macmillan Company, 1938.

MCVAUGH, ROGERS. *Edward Palmer, Plant Explorer of the American West.* Norman, University of Oklahoma Press, 1956.

PAGE, THOMAS J. *La Plata, the Argentine Confederation and Paraguay.* New York, Harper & Brothers, Publishers, 1859.

PALMER, EDWARD. "Food Products of the North American Indians," *Report of the Commissioner of Agriculture for the Year 1870,* 1871, pp. 404–428.

PALMER, EDWARD. *Original Unpublished Manuscripts (1865-1889).* Special Collections, University of Arizona Library, Tucson.

RIDGWAY, ROBERT. "Ornithology of Guadalupe Island Based on Notes and Collections Made by Dr. Edward Palmer," *U.S. Geological and Geographical Survey of the Territories,* Bulletin No. 2, 1876, pp. 183–196.

REIGEL, ROBERT E. *America Moves West,* 3rd ed. New York, Holt, Rinehart and Winston, Inc., 1956.

SAFFORD, WILLIAM E. "Edward Palmer," *Popular Science Monthly,* Vol. 78 (April, 1911), pp. 341–354.

STILL, BAYRD. *Mirror for Gotham.* New York, New York University Press, 1956.